SCIENTIFIC PROGRESS GOES "BOINK"

Other Books by Bill Watterson

Calvin and Hobbes
Something Under the Bed Is Drooling
Yukon Ho!
Weirdos From Another Planet!
The Revenge of the Baby-Sat

Treasury Collections

The Essential Calvin and Hobbes
The Calvin and Hobbes Lazy Sunday Book
The Authoritative Calvin and Hobbes

SCIENTIFIC PROGRESS GOES "BOINK"

A Calvin and Hobbes Collection by Bill Watterson

SCHOLASTIC INC.
New York Toronto London Auckland Sydney

Calvin and Hobbes is distributed internationally
by Universal Press Syndicate.

ISBN 0-590-45678-4

 Published by Scholastic Inc., 730 Broadway, New York, NY 10003, by arrangement with Andrews & McMeel, a Universal Press Syndicate Company.

12 11 10 9 8 7 6 5 4 3 2 1 9 10/0

Printed in the U.S.A.

First Scholastic Printing, January 1992

Printed on recycled paper.

Calvin and Hobbes

by WATTERSON

PHWPPT!

THPWIPBTH

AHHH..

DEAR, SOMETIME I WANT YOU TO LOOK AT THAT DISCOLORED SPOT ON THE RUG. IT SEEMS TO BE GETTING BIGGER ALL THE TIME.
MAY I LEAVE THE TABLE? LIKE RIGHT NOW?

I want that truck, Twinky.
IT'S MINE, MOE. I BROUGHT IT FROM HOME.

I said gimme the truck.
MOE, YOU CAN'T JUST ***TAKE*** THINGS FROM PEOPLE BECAUSE YOU'RE BIGGER!

I'm not taking it. You're **giving** it to me because we'll both be so much happier that way.

HOW TOUCHING.

MOE, GIVE ME MY TRUCK BACK. IT'S NOT YOURS.
It is **now**. You gave it to me.

I DIDN'T HAVE MUCH CHOICE, ***DID*** I?! IT WAS EITHER GIVE UP THE TRUCK OR GET PUNCHED!
So?

SO I ONLY "GAVE" IT TO YOU BECAUSE YOU'RE BIGGER AND MEANER THAN ME!
Yeah? ...So?

THE FORENSIC MARVEL HAS REDUCED MY LOGIC TO SHAMBLES.
You're saying you changed your mind about getting punched?

THAT NO-GOOD, ROTTEN MOE! HE WON'T GIVE MY TRUCK BACK TO ME. THE OAF WILL PROBABLY BREAK IT, TOO.

SHOULD I STEAL IT BACK? I KNOW STEALING IS WRONG, BUT ***HE*** STOLE IT FROM ***ME***, AND IF I **DON'T** STEAL IT BACK, MOE WILL JUST KEEP IT, AND THAT'S NOT FAIR.

THEY SAY TWO WRONGS DON'T MAKE A RIGHT, BUT WHAT ARE YOU SUPPOSED TO ***DO*** THEN? JUST LET THE BIGGEST GUY MAKE HIS OWN RULES ALL THE TIME? LET MIGHT MAKE RIGHT?

... THAT SOUNDS REASONABLE.

BY GOLLY, I AM GOING TO STEAL MY TRUCK BACK FROM MOE! IT'S MINE AND HE HAS NO RIGHT TO HAVE IT!
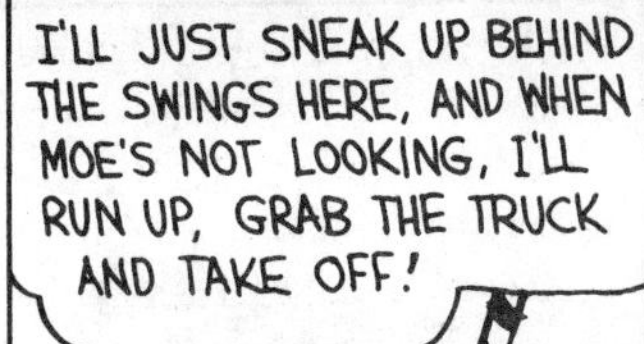
I'LL JUST SNEAK UP BEHIND THE SWINGS HERE, AND WHEN MOE'S NOT LOOKING, I'LL RUN UP, GRAB THE TRUCK AND TAKE OFF!

THIS PLAYGROUND SHOULD HAVE ONE OF THOSE AUTOMATIC INSURANCE MACHINES LIKE THEY HAVE IN AIRPORTS.

OK, MOE'S GOT HIS BACK TO ME! NOW I'LL ZIP OVER, STEAL MY TRUCK BACK AND RUN LIKE CRAZY!

HE'LL NEVER KNOW WHAT HIT HIM! BY THE TIME HE SEES THE TRUCK IS GONE, I'LL BE A MILE AWAY! IT'S A FAIL-PROOF PLAN! NOTHING CAN GO WRONG! IT'S A SNAP!

THERE'S NO REASON TO HESITATE. IT'LL BE OVER IN A SPLIT SECOND, AND I'LL SURE BE GLAD TO HAVE MY TRUCK BACK! I'LL JUST DO IT AND BE DONE! NOTHING TO IT! IT'S EASY!

OBVIOUSLY MY BODY DOESN'T BELIEVE A WORD MY BRAIN IS SAYING.

PHOOEY, WHO AM I KIDDING? I'D NEVER GET AWAY WITH STEALING MY TRUCK BACK FROM MOE. THE UGLY GALOOT IS THE SIZE OF A BUICK.

HMM... SINCE I CAN'T FIGHT HIM, MAYBE I SHOULD TRY TALKING TO HIM. MAYBE IF I REASONED WITH HIM, HE'D SEE MY SIDE.

MAYBE HE'D REALIZE THAT STEALING HURTS PEOPLE, AND MAYBE HE'D RETURN MY TRUCK WILLINGLY.
MAYBE IF I'M REALLY LUCKY I WON'T GO THROUGH LIFE WITH THE NICKNAME "OMELET FACE."

LISTEN, MOE, THAT'S **MY** TRUCK, AND I WANT IT BACK!
Yeah?

YEAH! IT'S MY FAVORITE TRUCK. YOU HAD NO RIGHT TO TAKE IT!
Yeah?

YEAH! SO GIVE IT BACK! **NOW!**
I'll fight you for it.

I'LL BET MY AUTOPSY REVEALS MY MOUTH IS TOO BIG.
C'mon, wimp!

I'M NOT GOING TO FIGHT YOU, MOE! IF YOU WON'T GIVE ME MY TRUCK BACK, **FINE!** GO AHEAD AND KEEP IT!

YOU'RE THE ONE WHO HAS TO LIVE WITH YOURSELF! **I** CAN'T MAKE YOU DO WHAT'S RIGHT! YOU CAN **HAVE** THE STUPID TRUCK!

OK, thanks! Heh heh.

HEY, KID, IF YOU'RE NOT GONNA SWING, GET OFF AND LET SOMEONE **ELSE** ON, HUH?

...SO MOE STOLE MY TRUCK, AND WHEN I TRIED TO GET IT BACK, MOE WANTED TO FIGHT ME FOR IT. I DIDN'T WANT TO FIGHT, SO I WALKED AWAY AND MOE KEPT MY TRUCK.

I DON'T UNDERSTAND IT, HOBBES. WHAT MAKES SOME PEOPLE SO GREEDY AND MEAN?

WHY IS IT THAT SOME PEOPLE DON'T CARE WHAT'S WRONG AND RIGHT? WHY DON'T PEOPLE TRY TO BE NICE TO EACH OTHER?

THE PROBLEM WITH PEOPLE IS THAT THEY'RE ONLY HUMAN.
WELL, **YOU'RE** LUCKY YOU DON'T HAVE TO **BE** ONE.

YOU KNOW, SOMETIMES THE WORLD SEEMS LIKE A PRETTY MEAN PLACE.
THAT'S WHY ANIMALS ARE SO SOFT AND HUGGY.

...YEAH...

MOM! MOMM!
Z

WHAT IS IT? WHAT'S THE MATTER?
HOBBES HAD A BAD DREAM.

YOU WOKE ME UP AT 2 A.M. BECAUSE YOU THINK YOUR STUFFED TIGER HAD A BAD DREAM?!?
HE DREAMED HE WAS SO HUNGRY, HE ATE US ALL UP.

I MUST BE HAVING A BAD DREAM.
DON'T YOU THINK YOU SHOULD MAKE HOBBES A SANDWICH, JUST IN CASE?

KNOW WHAT, DAD? AT THE FRESH FISH COUNTER IN THE SUPERMARKET, YOU CAN BUY REAL SQUID. THEY HAVE THEM IN A BUCKET.

THEY'RE REALLY GROSS.
MM, I'LL BET.

CALVIN, WHAT ARE YOU DOING?

Calvin and HOBBES
by WATTERSON
TIGERS ARE GREAT! THEY'RE THE TOAST OF THE TOWN. LIFE'S ALWAYS BETTER WHEN A TIGER'S AROUND!

CONSIDERING I OUTRANK YOU, I DON'T THINK I SHOULD HAVE TO DO THAT!

THIS MEETING OF THE TOP-SECRET CLUB G.R.O.S.S. (GET RID OF SLIMY GIRLS) WILL COME TO ORDER, SUPREME DICTATOR-FOR-LIFE CALVIN PRESIDING. ALL SALUTE!

OK, THE FIRST ORDER OF BUSINESS: PRESIDENT-AND-FIRST-TIGER HOBBES WILL READ THE MINUTES OF OUR LAST MEETING.

THANK YOU. 10:30 A.M.: READ MINUTES OF PREVIOUS MEETING. 10:31: DEBATED SO-CALLED "EDITORIAL SLANT" OF MINUTES. MUCH NONSENSE AND COMMOTION FROM DICTATOR-FOR-LIFE.
"NONSENSE"?!

10:32: PRESIDENT-AND-FIRST-TIGER OFFERS REASONABLE SOLUTION, BUT DICTATOR-FOR-LIFE TAKES NEEDLESS EXCEPTION.
REASONABLE SOLUTION?!? YOU TOLD ME TO GO JUMP IN A LAKE!

10:33: BLOWS EXCHANGED. DICTATOR-FOR-LIFE RECEIVES COMEUPPANCE.
HA! I BEAT YOU FAIR AND SQUARE! THESE MINUTES ARE NOTHING BUT LIES!

CALL ME A LIAR, WILL YOU?
BY GOLLY, I'LL CALL YOU WORSE THAN THAT!

CHOWDERHEAD!
MORON!
OGRE!
FLEABAG!

(PANT, PANT) TRUCE?
(GASP, PANT) OK, TRUCE.

WELL, ANOTHER PRODUCTIVE MEETING! WHAT A GREAT CLUB!
WATTERSON

HAVE YOU SEEN MY SHOES? I THOUGHT I HAD THEM OUT RIGHT HERE.

YOUR SHOES? I DON'T KNOW.
THEY WERE RIGHT HERE. WHERE COULD THEY HAVE GONE?

WE'RE GOING TO BE LATE.
WELL I CAN'T GO ANYWHERE WITHOUT MY SHOES. HELP ME LOOK.

THEY'RE NOT LEAVING US WITH A BABY SITTER TONIGHT!
WATTERSON

DING DONG
IT'S ROSALYN!
ANSWER THE DOOR, WILL YOU PLEASE, CALVIN?

HI ROZ. MY PARENTS CHANGED THEIR MINDS ABOUT GOING OUT, SO WE WON'T BE NEEDING YOUR SERVICES. GOODBYE.

HI, ROSALYN. WHAT ARE YOU TALKING ABOUT, CALVIN?
YOU CAN'T GO OUT IF MOM CAN'T FIND HER SHOES, RIGHT?

AND WHAT DO YOU KNOW ABOUT THAT?
I'D LIKE TO BE PAID IN ADVANCE TONIGHT.
UH, NOTHING! HA HA! UM, WHY? ARE HER SHOES MISSING?
WATTERSON

PHOOEY. MOM AND DAD LEFT. NOW WE'RE HERE ALONE WITH THE BABY SITTER FROM THE BLACK LAGOON.

HEE HEE! DO YOU THINK SHE REMEMBERS HOW LAST TIME WE THREATENED TO FLUSH HER SCIENCE NOTES DOWN THE TOILET?
HA HA HA! OUR FINEST MOMENT!

OK, YOU, GET IN BED.
WHAT?!
IT'S NOT EVEN 6:30!

SHE REMEMBERS, ALL RIGHT.
SHE CAN'T GET AWAY WITH THIS. WE'LL CALL THE RESCUE SQUAD.
WATTERSON

ROSALYN?
WHAT ARE YOU DOING OUT OF BED?

I THOUGHT I HEARD SOMETHING OUTSIDE.
I DIDN'T HEAR ANYTHING.

IT WAS KIND OF A THUMP. WILL YOU GO LOOK, AND MAKE SURE IT'S NOT ANYTHING SCARY?
I'LL CHECK, BUT I DIDN'T HEAR ANY THUMP.

YES...YES! GO OUT THE DOOR! TWO MORE STEPS! OH PLEASE, OH PLEASE! YES, YES, YES!
SEE? THERE'S NOTHING OUT HERE.

SEE, CALVIN? THERE'S NOTHING OUT HERE.
BUT I KNOW I HEARD SOMETHING! GO LOOK, OK? PLEASE?

OK, IF IT WILL MAKE YOU FEEL...
SLAM
HEY!

THIS WAS A TRICK?! WHY YOU SNEAKY LITTLE DRIP, I'LL GET YOU!!
HOBBES! I LOCKED HER OUT!

NOW WE CAN WATCH TV AND EAT COOKIES TILL WE'RE SICK! OH BOY!
THIS IS THE BEST WE'VE EVER BEEN BABY SAT!

CALVIN, YOU LET ME BACK IN THE HOUSE THIS INSTANT!

DON'T WORRY, ROSALYN! THERE'S ONLY A 50% CHANCE OF RAIN TONIGHT! HA HA!

SHE'S TRYING TO OPEN THE DOWNSTAIRS WINDOWS.
IT'S OK. I ALREADY LOCKED THEM.

YOU OPEN UP THAT DOOR!
HEY ROZ! WHAT'S IN YOUR PURSE? MIND IF WE LOOK??

CALVIN, I'M TELLING YOUR PARENTS ABOUT THIS! NOW LET ME IN!

PIPE DOWN, WILL YA ROZ? HOBBES AND I CAN HARDLY HEAR THE TV!

YOU'RE NOT SUPPOSED TO **BE** WATCHING TELEVISION!
HEY, IF YOU GO RENT US A VCR AND A MOVIE, WE'LL PUT THE TV NEAR A WINDOW SO YOU CAN WATCH TOO!

LET ME IN!
ARE YOU 18? YOU COULD GET US "VENUSIAN VAMPIRE VIXENS"!

CAL-VIN!
HANG ON, ROZ. THE PHONE IS RINGING!

I HOPE IT'S YOUR PARENTS! I HOPE THEY ASK TO TALK TO ME! BOY, YOU'LL BE IN TROUBLE **THEN**!

IT'S YOUR BOYFRIEND, CHARLIE! SHOULD I TELL HIM YOU'RE INDISPOSED? HA HA!

NO! LET ME TALK TO HIM!
SAY CHAS, DON'T YOU THINK YOU'RE SETTLING FOR TOO LITTLE IN THE GIRLFRIEND DEPARTMENT?

ISN'T IT GREAT TO GET OUT OF THE HOUSE ALONE TOGETHER FOR A CHANGE?
IT'S SO NICE AND QUIET. WE SHOULD DO THIS MORE OFTEN.

CALVIN, YOU'VE GOT FIVE SECONDS TO OPEN THE DOOR BEFORE I BREAK A WINDOW!
I'M TELLING YOU CHUCK, YOUR GIRLFRIEND IS A PSYCHO! I HOPE YOU'RE NOT MAKING ANY LONG-RANGE PLANS AROUND HER.

WOW, THIS IS FUN! ALL THE TV SHOWS WE'RE NOT ALLOWED TO WATCH, AND A BAG OF COOKIES EACH!
BLAM! BLAM! SCREEEEECHH!

SLAM!
HEY, WHAT WAS THAT?

AAUGH!!
ROSALYN!
H-HOW DID **YOU** G-GET IN??

GULP WHOOPS, I THINK IT'S PAST MY BEDTIME.

IT WAS ALL A MISUNDERSTANDING! AN INNOCENT MISTAKE! LET ME EXPLAIN!

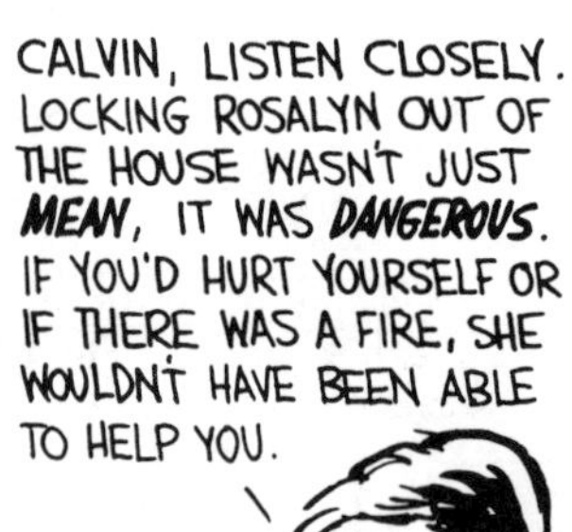
CALVIN, LISTEN CLOSELY. LOCKING ROSALYN OUT OF THE HOUSE WASN'T JUST **MEAN**, IT WAS **DANGEROUS**. IF YOU'D HURT YOURSELF OR IF THERE WAS A FIRE, SHE WOULDN'T HAVE BEEN ABLE TO HELP YOU.

YOU GO APOLOGIZE TO ROSALYN RIGHT NOW.

I-I'M SORRY, ROSALYN.
AND WE'RE SORRY TOO. I **PROMISE** YOU CALVIN WILL BEHAVE HIMSELF NEXT TIME.
AN EXTRA FIVE WOULD HELP THERE **BE** A NEXT TIME.

BOY, DID I GET IN TROUBLE.

STEALING MOM'S SHOES AND MAKING MOM AND DAD LATE... THEN LOCKING THE BABY SITTER OUT OF THE HOUSE... WHOOF.

THAT'S A LOT TO LIVE DOWN FOR JUST ONE EVENING. I FEEL PRETTY BAD.

AND HAVING EATEN A WHOLE PACKAGE OF OREOS DOESN'T HELP.
YOU SAID IT.

Calvin and HOBBES

by WATTERSON

GISZH! ... GISZH!...

..GISZH!

OH, NO! IT'S THE MIDDLE OF RECESS AND THERE'S A TYRANNOSAURUS ON THE PLAYGROUND!

THE KIDS AT THE TOP OF THE SLIDE ARE THE FIRST TO GO! HOW IRONIC THAT THEY HAD PUSHED AND FOUGHT EACH OTHER TO BE THERE!
!
!

PANDEMONIUM ENSUES! TEACHERS LINE THE KIDS UP TO GO INSIDE, BUT THAT PROVES TO BE A SAD MISTAKE!

WALKING QUIETLY IN SINGLE FILE, THE KIDS ARE GOBBLED UP LIKE CHILDREN McNUGGETS!

SOON THE PLAYGROUND IS EMPTY! IT'S ALL HIS! THE TYRANNOSAUR LETS OUT A TRIUMPHANT ROAR!

SAY, WHERE'S CALVIN? RECESS IS OVER. DIDN'T HE SEE US LINE UP TO COME IN?
I SEE HIM, MISS WORMWOOD! HE'S OUT BY THE SWINGS AND HE'S YELLING OR SOMETHING!

Calvin and Hobbes

by Watterson

THAT BIG, DUMB BULLY MOE PUNCHED ME AT SCHOOL YESTERDAY.

REALLY? WHAT DID YOU DO?

MAN, THIS IS BORING!

HOW AM I EVER GOING TO READ THREE WHOLE PAGES OF THIS BY TOMORROW?
IT'S IMPOSSIBLE!

... IMPOSSIBLE?? WHY, NOTHING'S IMPOSSIBLE!

NOT FOR... STUPENDOUS MAN!
BUM BA BA DAA DUM
BUM BA BA DAA DUM..

YES! IT'S... STUPENDOUS MAN! FRIEND OF FREEDOM! OPPONENT OF OPPRESSION! LOVER OF LIBERTY!

GREAT MOONS OF JUPITER! CALVIN (STUPENDOUS MAN'S 6-YEAR-OLD ALTER EGO) HAS THREE PAGES OF BORING HOMEWORK TO READ! IT'S TYRANNY!

ALTHOUGH STUPENDOUS MAN COULD EASILY READ THE ASSIGNMENT WITH STUPENDOUS HIGH-SPEED VISION, THE MASKED MAN OF MIGHT HAS A BOLDER PLAN!

WITH STUPENDOUS POWERS OF REASONING, THE CAPED COMBATANT CONCLUDES THERE'S NO NEED FOR HOMEWORK IF THERE'S NO SCHOOL TOMORROW!

A BLINDING BOLT OF BLAZING CRIMSON CAREENS ACROSS THE SKY! IT'S STUPENDOUS MAN!

SECONDS LATER, THE AMAZING MARVEL ALIGHTS UPON AN OBSERVATORY TELESCOPE AT MOUNT PALOMAR!

WITH STUPENDOUS STRENGTH, STUPENDOUS MAN CAREFULLY UNSCREWS THE GIANT LENS...

...AND BLASTS INTO SPACE WITH IT!

STUPENDOUS MAN CIRCLES THE EARTH WITH A 200-INCH TELESCOPE LENS!

ALIGNED PERFECTLY WITH THE SUN, THE MAGNIFYING LENS FOCUSES THE TERRIBLE SOLAR ENERGY...

...AND FRIES A CERTAIN ELEMENTARY SCHOOL CLEAN OFF THE MAP!

NOW MILD-MANNERED CALVIN HAS NO NEED TO DO HIS HOMEWORK EVER AGAIN! LIBERTY PREVAILS!
HOW'S YOUR HOMEWORK COMING, CALVIN?

UH OH, IT'S MY ARCH-NEMESIS, MOM-LADY! SHE CAN'T DISCOVER MY SECRET IDENTITY!
CALVIN? ARE YOU DOING YOUR HOMEWORK IN THERE?

QUICKLY, STUPENDOUS MAN LEAPS INTO THE CLOSET TO CHANGE BACK INTO HIS 6-YEAR-OLD ALTER EGO, MILD-MANNERED CALVIN!

CALVIN? ARE YOU IN HERE?
UNFORTUNATELY, STUPENDOUS MAN'S CAPE IS CAUGHT IN MILD-MANNERED CALVIN'S ZIPPER! CURSES!

THIS IS GOING TO BE A GOOD ONE, I CAN TELL.
GEEZ, MOM! CAN'T A GUY HAVE A LITTLE PRIVACY?!

AND WHY, MAY I ASK, ARE YOU STANDING IN YOUR UNDERWEAR IN THE CLOSET?
OH, NO REASON. UM... I WAS HOT.

YOU'RE SUPPOSED TO BE DOING YOUR HOMEWORK!
I DON'T NEED TO DO IT NOW, THANKS TO STUPENDOUS MAN!

OH YEAH?

IT WAS GREAT! HE FRIED THE SCHOOL WITH A BIG MAGNIFYING LENS IN SPACE! I'M SURE IT WILL BE IN ALL THE PAPERS TOMORROW.

BOY, SHE'LL BE IN TROUBLE WHEN SHE GIVES ME MY COSTUME BACK. BIG TROUBLE.

Calvin and HOBBES
by WATTERSON

I'M HO-OME!

POW

HI, CALVIN. WHATCHA DOIN'?
OOF, GET THIS BIG LUMMOX OFF ME.

LOOK AT YOU! YOU DIDN'T EVEN CHANGE OUT OF YOUR SCHOOL CLOTHES!
HOW COULD I ?! I DIDN'T EVEN GET IN THE DOOR!

EVERY DAY THIS MANIAC IS SO GLAD TO SEE ME THAT HE BLASTS OUT LIKE A BIG ORANGE TORPEDO! A DOG WILL JUST WAG ITS TAIL, BUT OF COURSE A TIGER HAS TO POUNCE ON YOU! STUPID ANIMAL!

HE POUNCES ON YOU?
OH, AND DON'T THINK HE DOESN'T ENJOY THE CUNNING AND TREACHERY OF IT ALL! TIGERS LIVE FOR THE THRILL OF A SNEAK ATTACK! IT'S THEIR EVIL NATURE!
WATTERSON

HE'S JUST SITTING THERE.
OH, SURE, BIG DISGUISE! LIKE NO ONE CAN FATHOM THE SAVAGE MIND OF A JUNGLE CAT! HA! HE'S A KILLER TO THE CORE!

I WISH MY PARENTS WOULD MOVE. MY DIARY IS GETTING WEIRDER EVERY DAY.
YEAH, YOU KNOW WHO I'M TALKING ABOUT! WIPE OFF THAT GRIN OR I'LL DO IT FOR YOU!

I'VE GOT AN IDEA, DAD.

MAYBE I'D GET BETTER GRADES IF YOU OFFERED ME $1 FOR EVERY "D", $5 FOR EVERY "C", $10 FOR EVERY "B", AND $50 FOR EVERY "A"!

I'M NOT GOING TO **BRIBE** YOU, CALVIN. YOU SHOULD APPLY YOURSELF FOR YOUR OWN GOOD.

RATS. I THOUGHT I COULD MAKE AN EASY FOUR BUCKS.

HELLO? VALLEY HARDWARE? YES, I'M CALLING TO SEE IF YOU SELL BLASTING CAPS, DETONATORS, TIMERS AND WIRE.

JUST THE WIRE? OK, FORGET IT. DO YOU RENT BULLDOZERS OR BACKHOES?

NO, NO, A ROTOTILLER WON'T DO AT ALL. I NEED SOMETHING MORE LIKE A WRECKING BALL. DO YOU KNOW WHERE I COULD GET ANYTHING LIKE THAT? NO? OK, GOODBYE.

LOOKS LIKE ANOTHER BORING DAY, HOBBES.

I CAN'T SLEEP, HOBBES. I'VE BEEN THINKING.
WHAT ABOUT?

WELL, SUPPOSE THERE'S NO AFTERLIFE. THAT WOULD MEAN **THIS** LIFE IS ALL YOU GET.

AND **THAT** WOULD MEAN I'M SITTING HERE IN BED AS PRECIOUS MOMENTS OF MY ALL-TOO-SHORT LIFE DISAPPEAR FOREVER.

HONEY, WAKE UP. DO YOU HEAR THE TELEVISION ON?

Calvin and HobbEs
by WATTERSON

GOSH, IT'S 1:30 AND I'M STILL AWAKE.

SOMEONE MUST'VE WAYLAID MR. SANDMAN.

I JUST CAN'T... GET... COMFORTABLE.

MMF.

I'M EXHAUSTED, BUT I CAN'T FALL ASLEEP.

MAYBE IF I JUST LIE STILL AND THINK ABOUT HOW GOOD IT FEELS TO BE IN BED, AND HOW SOFT THE PILLOW IS, AND HOW VERY, VERY TIRED I AM...

...PHOOEY. THIS ISN'T WORKING. ALL I WANT IS TO GET SOME SLEEP. THIS IS AWFUL.
CALVIN?

GEE MOM, ARE YOU AWAKE TOO?
IT'S TIME TO GET UP.

IT *CAN'T* BE! IT'S THE MIDDLE OF THE NIGHT AND I HAVEN'T SLEPT A WINK YET!
CALVIN?

Z
HUZBGH
C'MON, UP AND AT 'EM.

blink
blink

THIS IS GOING TO BE A BAD DAY.

THE STRANGEST THING HAPPENED TO ME A FEW MINUTES AGO.
OH? WHAT?

I WAS MINDING MY OWN BUSINESS, WHEN SUDDENLY I WAS ZAPPED INTO SOME SORT OF SPACE VOID VORTEX!

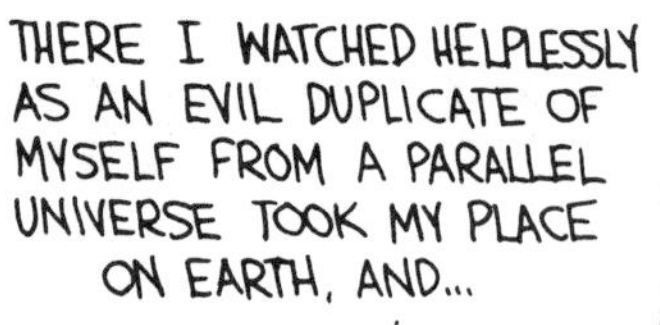
THERE I WATCHED HELPLESSLY AS AN EVIL DUPLICATE OF MYSELF FROM A PARALLEL UNIVERSE TOOK MY PLACE ON EARTH, AND...

WHAT HAVE YOU DONE **NOW**?
NO, NO, SEE, IT WASN'T **ME**...
WATTERSON

HEH HEH HEH!

AHA! I SEE YOU! SNEAKING UP TO POUNCE ON ME, EH?

PHOOEY.
YOU SEE WHY **MOST** TIGERS DON'T CHUCKLE TO THEMSELVES.
WATTERSON

WANT TO PLAY A GREAT GAME I INVENTED?
OK.

IT'S CALLED "GROSS OUT." YOU SAY THE GROSSEST THING YOU CAN IMAGINE, AND THEN I TRY TO THINK OF SOMETHING EVEN GROSSER.

WHOEVER COMES UP WITH THE GROSSEST THING GETS A POINT, AND WE PLAY UNTIL SOMEONE GETS 50 POINTS, OK?

I THINK I ALREADY KNOW WHO'S GOING TO WIN.
IT'S WEIRD. NOBODY HAS EVER PLAYED A WHOLE GAME WITH ME.
WATTERSON

Calvin and HOBBES
by WATTERSON
WOW, HONEY, YOU'RE MISSING A BEAUTIFUL SUNSET OUT HERE!

I'LL COUNT TO 10, AND THEN... POW!

DAD, HOW COME OLD PHOTOGRAPHS ARE ALWAYS BLACK AND WHITE? DIDN'T THEY HAVE COLOR FILM BACK THEN?

SURE THEY DID. IN FACT, THOSE OLD PHOTOGRAPHS ARE IN COLOR. IT'S JUST THE WORLD WAS BLACK AND WHITE THEN.

REALLY?
YEP. THE WORLD DIDN'T TURN COLOR UNTIL SOMETIME IN THE 1930s, AND IT WAS PRETTY GRAINY COLOR FOR A WHILE, TOO.

THAT'S REALLY WEIRD.
WELL, TRUTH IS STRANGER THAN FICTION.

BUT THEN WHY ARE OLD PAINTINGS IN COLOR?! IF THE WORLD WAS BLACK AND WHITE, WOULDN'T ARTISTS HAVE PAINTED IT THAT WAY?
NOT NECESSARILY. A LOT OF GREAT ARTISTS WERE INSANE.

BUT... BUT HOW COULD THEY HAVE PAINTED IN COLOR ANYWAY? WOULDN'T THEIR PAINTS HAVE BEEN SHADES OF GRAY BACK THEN?
OF COURSE, BUT THEY TURNED COLORS LIKE EVERYTHING ELSE DID IN THE '30s.

SO WHY DIDN'T OLD BLACK AND WHITE PHOTOS TURN COLOR TOO?
BECAUSE THEY WERE COLOR PICTURES OF BLACK AND WHITE, REMEMBER?

THE WORLD IS A COMPLICATED PLACE, HOBBES.
WHENEVER IT SEEMS THAT WAY, I TAKE A NAP IN A TREE AND WAIT FOR DINNER.
WATTERSON

PAY ATTENTION TO ME.

I'VE GOT TO WRITE A REPORT FOR SCHOOL.

WHAT'S YOUR TOPIC?
BATS. CAN YOU IMAGINE ANYTHING MORE STUPID?

HECK, *I* DON'T KNOW ANYTHING ABOUT BATS! HOW AM I SUPPOSED TO WRITE A REPORT ON A SUBJECT I KNOW NOTHING ABOUT?! IT'S IMPOSSIBLE!

I SUPPOSE RESEARCH IS OUT OF THE QUESTION.
OH, LIKE I'M GOING TO LEARN ABOUT BATS AND ***THEN*** WRITE A REPORT?! GIVE ME A BREAK!

HELLO, SUSIE? THIS IS CALVIN. YOU KNOW THIS REPORT WE'RE SUPPOSED TO WRITE FOR SCHOOL? YEAH. MY TOPIC IS BATS. WHAT'S YOURS?

ELEPHANTS? HMM. WELL, ARE YOU GOING TO THE LIBRARY TO LOOK UP ELEPHANTS? YOU ARE? GREAT!

WHILE YOU'RE THERE, COULD YOU RESEARCH BATS TOO, AND MAKE COPIES OF ALL THE INFORMATION YOU FIND, AND MAYBE UNDERLINE THE IMPORTANT PARTS FOR ME, AND SORT OF OUTLINE IT, SO I WOULDN'T HAVE TO READ IT ALL?

HOW'D IT GO?
I REALLY LOATHE GIRLS.

I GUESS YOU WON'T BE SETTING THE GRADE CURVE **THIS** TIME, SUSIE! READ IT AND WEEP.

"BATS: THE BIG BUG SCOURGE OF THE SKIES."

"DUSK! WITH A CREEPY, TINGLING SENSATION, YOU HEAR THE FLUTTERING OF LEATHERY WINGS! BATS! WITH GLOWING RED EYES AND GLISTENING FANGS, THESE UNSPEAKABLE GIANT BUGS DROP ONTO..."

Calvin and HOBBES
by WATTERSON
I'VE BEEN THINKING, HOBBES.

ON A WEEKEND?
WELL, IT WASN'T ON PURPOSE..

I BELIEVE HISTORY IS A FORCE.

ITS UNALTERABLE TIDE SWEEPS ALL PEOPLE AND INSTITUTIONS ALONG ITS UNRELENTING PATH. EVERYTHING AND EVERYONE SERVES HISTORY'S SINGLE PURPOSE.

AND WHAT IS THAT PURPOSE?
WHY, TO PRODUCE ME, OF COURSE! I'M THE END RESULT OF HISTORY.

YOU?
THINK OF IT! THOUSANDS OF GENERATIONS LIVED AND DIED TO PRODUCE MY EXACT, SPECIFIC PARENTS, WHOSE REASON FOR BEING, OBVIOUSLY, WAS TO PRODUCE ME.

ALL HISTORY UP TO THIS POINT HAS BEEN SPENT PREPARING THE WORLD FOR MY PRESENCE.
HMM, 4½ BILLION YEARS PROBABLY WASN'T LONG ENOUGH.

NOW I'M HERE, AND HISTORY IS VINDICATED.
SO NOW THAT HISTORY'S BROUGHT YOU, WHAT ARE YOU GOING TO DO?

OOH, YOU WASCAWWY WABBIT!

Calvin and Hobbes

by WATTERSON

CRIICKK

I SURE WISH IT WOULD SNOW.

WHAT'S WITH THE SLED? THERE'S NO SNOW.

I AIM TO FIX *THAT* RIGHT NOW WITH AN APPEAL TO THE SNOW DEMONS.
SNOW DEMONS?

OBVIOUSLY THEY'RE TORMENTING US WITH THIS WIMPY WEATHER BECAUSE THEY'RE ANGRY. WE MUST APPEASE THEM.

OH.
I'M GOING TO LIE HERE ON MY SLED AND THINK SNOW THOUGHTS UNTIL THE SNOW DEMONS HAVE MERCY AND UNLEASH A BLIZZARD.

SNOW, SNOW! HIGH AND LOW! WHEREVER WE GO! LET IT BLOW! TO AND FRO! HI-DE-HO! SNOW! SNOW! SNOW!

WELL, I'LL COME OUT IN EARLY JANUARY AND SEE HOW YOU'RE DOING.
TELL MOM I'LL NEED MY MEALS OUT HERE AND I WON'T BE GOING TO SCHOOL TOMORROW.
WATTERSON

HI SUSIE. WHAT DID YOU BRING FOR LUNCH TODAY?
A SWISS CHEESE AND KETCHUP SANDWICH.

IT'S MY VERY FAVORITE, TOO, SO I DON'T WANT TO HEAR WHAT GROSS THING **YOU** BROUGHT.
RELAX, SUSIE. I BOUGHT THE CAFETERIA LUNCH TODAY.

GOOD.
IT APPEARS TO BE CIGAR BUTTS IN A GALLSTONE SAUCE.

THAT'S BEANY-WIENIES!
REALLY? OH GROSS.

HELLO?
HI, DAD. IT'S ME, CALVIN.

YOU'RE SUPPOSED TO BE AT SCHOOL!
I **AM** AT SCHOOL.

ARE YOU ALL RIGHT? WHAT'S THE MATTER? WHY ARE YOU CALLING?

I TOLD THE TEACHER I HAD TO GO TO THE BATHROOM. QUICK, WHAT'S 11+7?

I WAS READING ABOUT HOW COUNTLESS SPECIES ARE BEING PUSHED TOWARD EXTINCTION BY MAN'S DESTRUCTION OF FORESTS.

SOMETIMES I THINK THE SUREST SIGN THAT INTELLIGENT LIFE EXISTS ELSEWHERE IN THE UNIVERSE IS THAT NONE OF IT HAS TRIED TO CONTACT US.

WHAT ARE YOU DOING?! YOU'RE GOING TO BE LATE FOR SCHOOL! HURRY UP AND PUT YOUR CLOTHES ON RIGHT!

IT'S SAD HOW SOME PEOPLE CAN'T HANDLE A LITTLE VARIETY.

I WONDER WHY MAN WAS PUT ON EARTH. WHAT'S OUR PURPOSE? WHY ARE WE HERE?

TIGER FOOD.

Z

Z

SNAP

A LITTLE HIGH-STRUNG, ARE WE?
WE TIGERS CALL IT LIGHTNING QUICK REFLEXES.

Calvin and HOBBES

by WATTERSON

TRIP!

AAAAAA

POOF

WATTERSON

AAAAA

POOF

CALVIN? ARE YOU GETTING UP?

SIGHHHH...

HEY! WHOA! WHOAA!

WAHHH!

BAM
CALVIN, QUIT BANGING AROUND!

OW! WHAT AM I DOING ON THE CEILING?

HMM... NOTHING ELSE FELL UP. JUST ME. THIS IS VERY STRANGE.

EVEN IF I TRY TO JUMP TO THE FLOOR, I LAND BACK ON THE CEILING! MY PERSONAL GRAVITY MUST HAVE REVERSED POLARITY!

YOU'D THINK THIS WOULD BE THE TYPE OF THING WE'D LEARN ABOUT IN SCIENCE CLASS, BUT NO, WE LEARN ABOUT CIRRUS CLOUDS.

HAVING MY PERSONAL GRAVITY POLARITY REVERSED IS A REAL NUISANCE. HOW AM I GOING TO GET UP TO THE FLOOR?

THERE'S NOT ANYTHING ON THE CEILING THAT I COULD EVEN CLIMB UP.
HOW AM I SUPPOSED TO DO MY HOMEWORK WHEN I'M TRAPPED ON THE CEILING? IT'S IMPOSSIBLE.

WATTERSON

MOM AND DAD WON'T BE TOO HAPPY ABOUT **THIS**. NO SIR.

DAD WILL HAVE TO BOLT MY BED TO THE CEILING TONIGHT, AND MOM WILL HAVE TO STAND ON A STEPLADDER TO HAND ME DINNER.

THEN I'LL HAVE TO HOLD MY PLATE UPSIDE-DOWN ABOVE MY HEAD AND SCRAPE THE FOOD OFF THE UNDERSIDE! AND IF I SPILL ANYTHING, IT WILL FLY 10 FEET UP TO THE FLOOR AND SPLOT!

THIS IS GOING TO BE THE MOST FUN I'VE EVER HAD!

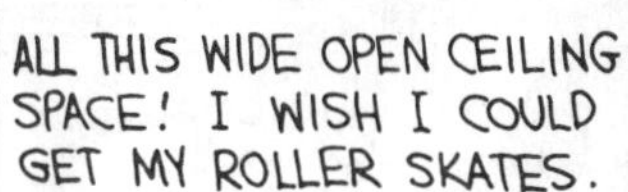
ALL THIS WIDE OPEN CEILING SPACE! I WISH I COULD GET MY ROLLER SKATES.

HEY, MAYBE I CAN CLIMB UP THIS BOOKCASE AND WHEN I GET TO THE BOTTOM SHELF, LEAP TO A CHAIR!

THEN I CAN PULL MYSELF ACROSS TO OTHER PIECES OF FURNITURE AND WORK MY WAY TO MY TOY CHEST.

...I CAN HEAR MOM NOW: "HOW ON EARTH DID YOU GET SNEAKER PRINTS ON THE UNDERSIDE OF EACH SHELF?!"

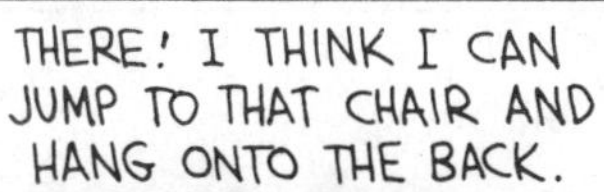
THERE! I THINK I CAN JUMP TO THAT CHAIR AND HANG ONTO THE BACK.

GEERONIMOOO!

WHOAAA!

WHAM!
GREAT. JUST GREAT.
CALVIN, QUIT BANGING AROUND!

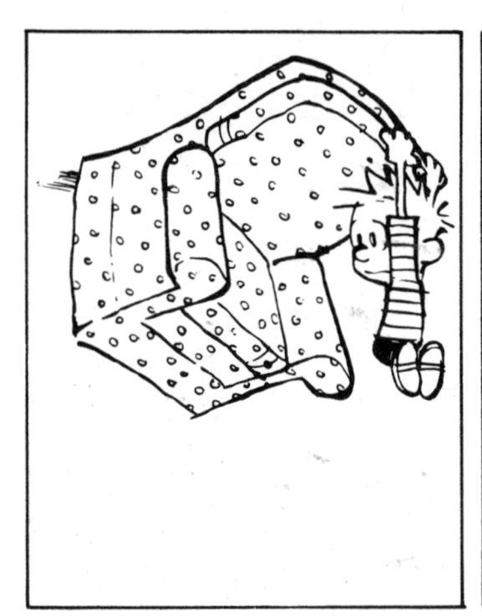

RRG!
MMF!

GETTING ANY HOMEWORK DONE, OR ARE YOU JUST RUINING FURNITURE?
MAYBE I'M HANGING HERE FOR DEAR LIFE! EVER THINK OF THAT?

I'M TELLING YOU, MY PERSONAL GRAVITY REVERSED ITS POLARITY! I FALL UP NOW!

I'VE BEEN TRAPPED ON THE CEILING! I COULDN'T DO MY HOMEWORK UP THERE! MY DESK IS ON THE FLOOR!

YOU SHOULD BE GLAD I WASN'T OUTSIDE WHEN IT HAPPENED, OR I'D BE SAILING THROUGH THE IONOSPHERE!

RIGHT. NOW I DON'T WANT TO HEAR ANY MORE NONSENSE UNTIL YOU'RE THROUGH WITH YOUR HOMEWORK, UNDERSTAND?
DON'T LET GO! DON'T LET GO!

IT'S... IT'S A MIRACLE! MY PERSONAL GRAVITY IS BACK TO NORMAL!
GLAD TO HEAR IT. NOW DO YOUR MATH.

YOU BET, MOM. BOY, WHAT A RELIEF TO BE PULLED DOWN INSTEAD OF UP!
I'LL CHECK YOUR PROGRESS IN A LITTLE BIT.
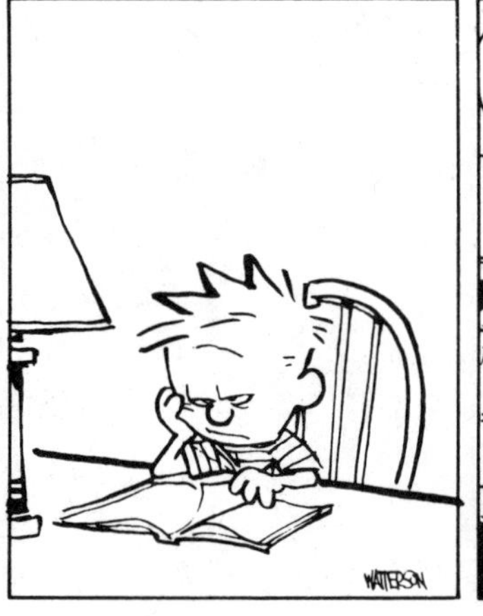

UH OH.

THIS HAS BEEN A MOST PECULIAR AFTERNOON.

I'VE GOT TO GET OUT-SIDE BEFORE I GROW BIGGER!

I SUPPOSE I SHOULD GET MY PITUITARY GLAND CHECKED.

I KNOW! I'LL RUN DOWN-TOWN AND FIND DAD AT WORK! MAYBE HE CAN HELP!

HMM... NOW WHICH BUILDING DOES DAD WORK IN? THEY ALL LOOK THE SAME.

...WELL, MAYBE DAD CAN FIND **ME**.

WELL? HOW'S YOUR MATH COMING ALONG?
I'VE ALMOST STARTED!

OH BROTHER! ANOTHER "DISCUSSION" ABOUT MY STUDY HABITS AND THE IMPORTANCE OF HOMEWORK.

I TRIED EXPLAINING THAT IT'S HARD TO STUDY WHEN ONE'S SIZE SUDDENLY STARTS INCREASING, BUT DOES SHE CARE?! HAH!

NO, IT'S JUST BLAH BLAH BLAH, LIKE IT'S ALL MY FAULT! MOM'S NEVER BEEN AS BIG AS A GALAXY, SO SHE CAN'T UNDERSTAND HOW ANYONE ELSE COULD BE! SHEEESH.

OOPS, IT LOOKS LIKE SHE'S WRAPPING UP. BETTER START NODDING.
GOOD. I'M GLAD WE HAD THIS LITTLE TALK.

DOING HOMEWORK?
YEAHHHH... BOY, YOU MISSED THE SHOW.

I GOT A BIG LECTURE FROM MOM JUST BECAUSE I GOT STUCK ON THE CEILING AND THEN GREW SO BIG I FELL OFF THE PLANET WHEN I WAS SUPPOSED TO BE DOING MY MATH!

GEE, THAT'S NOT VERY FAIR.
YOU SAID IT. HERE, HOW ABOUT HELPING ME HURRY UP WITH THESE PROBLEMS?
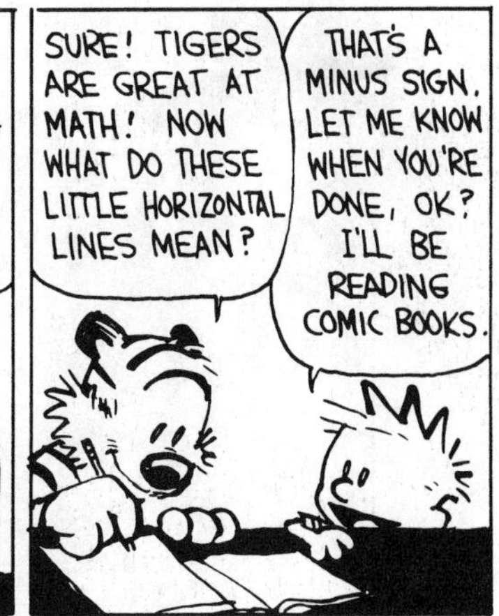
SURE! TIGERS ARE GREAT AT MATH! NOW WHAT DO THESE LITTLE HORIZONTAL LINES MEAN?
THAT'S A MINUS SIGN. LET ME KNOW WHEN YOU'RE DONE, OK? I'LL BE READING COMIC BOOKS.

Calvin and Hobbes
by WATTERSON
OUT IN THE FARTHEST REACHES OF THE GALAXY ZOOMS INTERPLANETARY EXPLORER, SPACEMAN SPIFF!

OOH, NICE SCENERY!

THE MUCK MONSTERS OF MORDO ARE CLOSING IN ON OUR HERO! A FIERY FLASH OF FATALITY-FLARE MISSES BY MERE MICROMIPS!

SPIFF'S DESPERATE GAMBIT: TO FLY THROUGH THE RINGS OF PLANET ZK-5 BELOW! OUR HERO THROTTLES THE THRUSTERS AND DIVES!

IT WORKS! THE MUCK MONSTERS VEER OFF, AFRAID TO FOLLOW THE FEARLESS SPIFF INTO THE FROZEN FRAGMENTS OF ICE AND ROCK!

SWERVING LEFT, RIGHT, UP, AND DOWN, THE AMAZING SPACEMAN SPIFF PILOTS AROUND EACH HURLING MISSILE! WHAT SKILL! WHAT FORTITU...

POW!
OH NO! OUR HERO IS GOING DOWN!!

Got 'im! Heh heh!
THOSE DARN LITTLE GUYS ARE HARD TO HIT, AREN'T THEY?
I HATE PLAYING "DODGE BALL" IN GYM CLASS.
WATTERSON

WHEN ARE WE GOING TO GET A CHRISTMAS TREE?
OH, I DUNNO. PROBABLY A LITTLE AFTER NEW YEAR'S.

AFTER NEW YEAR'S?
SURE. WE CAN JUST GO UP THE STREET AND PICK THE BEST TREE FROM THE NEIGHBORS' DRIVEWAYS.

WHAT?!
SOMETIMES THERE'S STILL TINSEL ON THE TREE TOO, SO YOU DON'T EVEN HAVE TO DECORATE IT! WE'LL SAVE TIME AND MONEY!

OK, WHAT DID YOUR DAD TELL YOU THIS TIME?

YES, CALVIN? YOU HAVE A QUESTION?

YEAH, I WAS WONDERING IF WE COULD STOP THE LESSON HERE AND ADJOURN TO THE PLAYGROUND FOR THE REST OF THE DAY.

OF COURSE NOT. NOW THEN, LET'S ALL TURN TO PAGE 24 AND...
MISS WORMWOOD?

YES?
HOW ABOUT JUST ME THEN?

FOR "SHOW AND TELL" TODAY, I HAVE SOMETHING THAT WILL ASTOUND AND AMAZE YOU! THIS LITTLE GUY CAN...

HAVE YOU ALL HAD YOUR SHOTS?

Calvin and HOBBES
by WATTERSON
DEAR SANTA,
HOW ARE YOU?
WELL, ENOUGH CHIT CHAT. LET'S GET DOWN TO BUSINESS.
THIS YEAR I WANT...

WILL YOU DRIVE TO WORK AND FAX MY CHRISTMAS LIST TO SANTA?

THAT'S A BIG ENVELOPE. ARE YOU MAILING A BOOK?
THIS IS MY CHRISTMAS LIST. CAN YOU BELIEVE THIS IS COSTING ME $2.40 TO SEND?

YES.
WELL, AT THIS PRICE, ALL I CAN SAY IS THAT SANTA HAD BETTER READ IT DARN CAREFULLY. LAST YEAR I DIDN'T GET HALF OF WHAT I WANTED.

HAVE YOU BEHAVED ANY BETTER THIS YEAR?
IT DEPENDS HOW YOU... HEY, JUST WHAT ARE YOU INSINUATING?! WHY, I'LL HAVE YOU KNOW I'VE BEEN A VERITABLE ANGEL THIS YEAR, JUST LIKE ALWAYS!

IN THAT CASE, WE CAN HAVE A COOKOUT WITH YOUR STOCKING CONTENTS.
DON'T GET SMART, BUB, OR I'LL WALLOP YOU ON THE 26TH.

DID YOU PUT ANYTHING ON YOUR LIST FOR ME?
WHAT, AND PAY MORE POSTAGE? THIS PACKAGE IS BREAKING MY ARMS ALREADY! GO WRITE YOUR OWN LIST!

TIDINGS OF COMFORT AND JOY TO YOU TOO.
LOOK, IT'S EVERY MAN FOR HIMSELF IN THIS WORLD. NOW GIVE ME A BOOST, WILL YA?
WATTERSON

NO, IT'S TOO MUCH TROUBLE. **FIRST** I'D HAVE TO GET UP. **THEN** I'D HAVE TO PUT ON A COAT. **THEN** I'D HAVE TO FIND MY HAT AND PUT **IT** ON. (SIGH) THEN WE'D RUN AROUND AND I'D GET TIRED, AND WHEN WE CAME IN I'D HAVE TO TAKE ALL THAT STUFF **OFF**. NO WAY.

I'LL TELL YOUR MOM TO TURN YOU TOWARD THE LIGHT AND WATER YOU PERIODICALLY.

INSTEAD OF MAKING SMART REMARKS, YOU COULD GET ME THE REMOTE CONTROL.

Calvin and Hobbes

by WATTERSON

KNOW WHAT THIS IS?

WHAT ARE YOU DOING STILL IN BED?! I'VE CALLED YOU THREE TIMES! YOU'RE GOING TO MISS THE BUS!

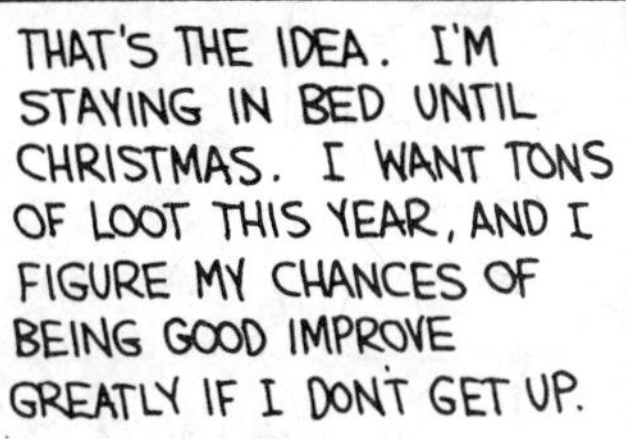
THAT'S THE IDEA. I'M STAYING IN BED UNTIL CHRISTMAS. I WANT TONS OF LOOT THIS YEAR, AND I FIGURE MY CHANCES OF BEING GOOD IMPROVE GREATLY IF I DON'T GET UP.

DISOBEYING YOUR MOTHER AND MISSING THE BUS ISN'T GOOD. IT'S BAD.

THAT DARN SANTA HAS GOT ME EVERY WAY I TURN.

I HATE THIS TIME OF YEAR. I'VE GOT TO BE GOOD FOR TWO MORE WEEKS IF I WANT ANY GOODIES THIS CHRISTMAS! I'LL NEVER MAKE IT.

I *TRY* TO BE GOOD! I *DO*! MY HEART IS AS PURE AS DRIVEN SNOW!
IT'S JUST THAT, WELL, SOMETIMES EVENTS BEYOND MY CONTROL CONSPIRE AGAINST ME!

I'M USUALLY AN INNOCENT BYSTAND... *HEY*, I *SAW* YOU ROLL YOUR EYES! SO YOU DON'T BELIEVE ME, EH?!
ME??

BY GOLLY, EACH OF YOUR EYES WILL BE ROLLING TOWARD THE OTHER WHEN *I'M* THROUGH WITH YOU!
HA! I HOPE YOU ASKED SANTA FOR SOME CRUTCHES!
OOF!
ZING

MISERABLE MISCREANT! QUESTION MY INTEGRITY, WILL YOU?
I CAN'T *QUESTION* IT UNTIL I SEE SOME *EVIDENCE* OF IT!

AUGHH! I'VE BEEN *FIGHTING*!
ONLY IN THE LOOSEST SENSE OF THE WORD.

SANTA, HE *MADE* ME! I DIDN'T *MEAN* TO FIGHT!
YES HE DID! YES HE DID! HE STARTED IT!

I DID *NOT*!
DID TOO!
DID NOT!
DID TOO!
LIAR!
LIAR!

LOOK HOBBES, NO ONE **SAW** US FIGHTING, RIGHT? THIS CAN BE **OUR** LITTLE **SECRET**, OK? SANTA DOESN'T HAVE TO KNOW ABOUT THIS, RIGHT?
MAYBE HE DOES AND MAYBE HE DOESN'T.

OK, OK, I'LL EVEN APOLOGIZE! I'M SORRY. HOW'S THAT? SEE, IT'S OK TO FIGHT JUST A LITTLE BIT IF YOU SAY YOU'RE SORRY AFTERWARD.
YOU BIT AND KICKED.

I **SAID** I WAS SORRY! WHAT MORE DO YOU WANT?!
YOU COULD LET ME READ ALL YOUR COMIC BOOKS.

OVER MY DEAD BODY!
"DEAR SANTA, KNOW WHAT CALVIN DID TODAY?"

BOY, IF IT WASN'T SO CLOSE TO CHRISTMAS, I'D POUND YOU GOOD!
YEAH, I'D LIKE TO SEE YOU TRY!

OH NO YOU DON'T! YOU'RE NOT TEMPTING **ME**! I WANT EVERY ITEM ON MY CHRISTMAS LIST, SO I'M BEING **GOOD**, NO MATTER WHAT THE PROVOCATION!

HERE COMES SUSIE DERKINS.
REALLY? QUICK, HELP ME FIND A PINE CONE I CAN THROW AT..

..**NO**! I'M BEING **GOOD**! GOOD! GOOD! GOOD!
YOU'LL NEVER MAKE IT TILL CHRISTMAS. GIVE UP NOW AND ENJOY YOURSELF.

HI CALVIN. ARE YOU BRINGING YOUR STUFFED TIGER TO SCHOOL TODAY?
NO, HE'S JUST KEEPING ME COMPANY WHILE I WAIT FOR THE BUS.

OH.
BUT ACTUALLY, HE'S BEEN NOTHING BUT TROUBLE TODAY. HE'S TRYING TO SABOTAGE MY CHRISTMAS BY MAKING ME BE BAD INSTEAD OF GOOD.

FORTUNATELY, I ASKED SANTA FOR SUCH GREAT PRESENTS THAT I CAN WITHSTAND ANY TEMPTATION. I'M BEING AN ABSOLUTE ANGEL.

WHAT DID YOU ASK FOR?
A HEAT-SEEKING GUIDED MISSILE. I FIGURE FIVE MINUTES WITH ONE OF **THOSE** BABIES WILL MAKE UP FOR THIS WHOLE ROTTEN MONTH.

Calvin and HOBBES

by WATTERSON

'TIS THE SEASON TO ADVERTISE.

CALVIN, LOOK! YOU GOT A LETTER!
A LETTER? I DIDN'T HEAR THE MAIL TRUCK. A LETTER FOR ME?

THE RETURN ADDRESS SAYS "NORTH POLE".
OH MY GOSH, IT MUST BE FROM SANTA! SANTA SENT ME A LETTER! WOW! GEE!

READ IT! READ IT!
"DEAR CALVIN, YOU ROTTEN LITTLE KID..."
OH NO!! SANTA CALLED ME ROTTEN! I'M DOOMED!

KEEP READING.
"I MADE A LIST, BUT I DIDN'T BOTHER CHECKING IT TWICE, BECAUSE OBVIOUSLY YOU'RE THE NAUGHTIEST KID IN THE WHOLE WORLD."
AUGH!

WHAT ELSE?
"I'M WRITING TO GIVE YOU ONE LAST CHANCE. YOU'VE GOT SEVEN DAYS TO GET ON THE 'GOOD BOY' LIST."
SEVEN DAYS!! OH NO! WHAT CAN I DO??

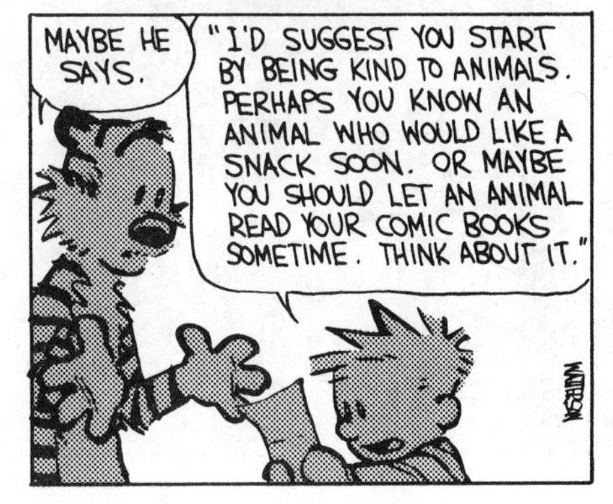

MAYBE HE SAYS.
"I'D SUGGEST YOU START BY BEING KIND TO ANIMALS. PERHAPS YOU KNOW AN ANIMAL WHO WOULD LIKE A SNACK SOON. OR MAYBE YOU SHOULD LET AN ANIMAL READ YOUR COMIC BOOKS SOMETIME. THINK ABOUT IT."
WATTERSON

SOUNDS LIKE SAGE ADVICE.
"SIGNED, SANTA CLAWS."
SANTA CLAWS? WAIT A MINUTE! I RECOGNIZE THIS HANDWRITING! IT'S YOURS! SANTA DIDN'T WRITE THIS AT ALL!!

GIVE YOU A SNACK, HUH?! HOW ABOUT A KNUCKLE SANDWICH?!
HMPH. WELL, IT'S WHAT SANTA WOULD'VE WRITTEN IF HE WASN'T SO BUSY NOW.

WANT TO HELP ME WRITE A BOOK?
SURE. WHAT'S IT ABOUT?

WELL, YOU KNOW WHAT HISTORICAL FICTION IS? THIS IS SORT OF LIKE THAT. I'M WRITING A FICTIONAL AUTOBIOGRAPHY.

IT'S THE STORY OF MY LIFE, BUT WITH A LOT OF PARTS COMPLETELY MADE UP.
WHY WOULD YOU MAKE UP YOUR OWN LIFE?

BECAUSE IN MY BOOK I HAVE A FLAME THROWER!
WATTERSON

STILL AND QUIET FELINE FORM, IN THE SUN, ASLEEP AND WARM. HIS TAIL IS LIMP, HIS WHISKERS DROOPED. MAN, WHAT COULD MAKE THIS CAT SO POOPED?

SHEESHH..
WATTERSON

HI MOM! I'M MAKING MY OWN NEWSPAPER TO REPORT THE EVENTS OF OUR HOUSEHOLD.
THAT'S NICE.

NOW I'M LOOKING FOR A PAGE ONE LEAD STORY. CAN I INTERVIEW YOU?
SURE.
WATTERSON

OK, WHAT ARE YOU CUTTING UP THERE FOR DINNER?
FISH.

KNIFE WIELDING MOTHER HACKS ICHTHYOID! GRIM MELEE IS EVENING RITUAL! SUBURBAN FAMILY DEVOURS VICTIM!
OUT OF THE KITCHEN! OUT! OUT!

HI DAD. I'M MAKING MY OWN NEWSPAPER TO REPORT THE EVENTS OF OUR HOUSEHOLD. WOULD YOU HELP ME OUT?
SURE, WHAT DO YOU NEED?

WELL, YOU CAN TAKE YOUR PICK. EITHER YOU CAN GIVE ME 15 BUCKS TO PAY MY LABOR AND PRODUCTION COSTS...
15 BUCKS?!

...OR YOU CAN BE THE SUBJECT OF A COMIC STRIP CALLED "DOPEY DAD."

SO IN THE NEXT PANEL, DOPEY DAD YELLS, "IT'S BED-TIME FOR YOU, YOUNG MAN!"
HEE HEE! LOOK HOW BIG I MADE HIS MOUTH!

OOH HAHH
OOH HAHH

OOH HAHH
OOH HAHH

OOH HAHH
OOH HAHHH

I WISH WE'D GED AD AQUARIUB!

WHAT STORY WOULD YOU LIKE TONIGHT, CALVIN?
HAMSTER HUEY AND THE GOOEY KABLOOIE!

OH NO, NOT AGAIN! THAT'S WHAT YOU HEAR EVERY NIGHT! LET'S READ SOMETHING DIFFERENT.
I WANT HAMSTER HUEY! I WANT HAMSTER HUEY!

C'MON, WE'LL READ A NEW STORY TONIGHT. YOU'LL LIKE IT, I PROMISE.
NO I WON'T! I'LL STAY AWAKE UNTIL MORNING IF YOU DON'T READ HAMSTER HUEY!

I DIDN'T REMEMBER HAMSTER HUEY HAVING QUITE THAT SARCASTIC TONE OF VOICE.
OR DOING EVERYTHING SO FAST.

Calvin and Hobbes
by WATTERSON
Christmas Eve
ON WINDOW PANES, THE ICY FROST
LEAVES FEATHERED PATTERNS, CRISSED & CROSSED,
BUT IN OUR HOUSE THE CHRISTMAS TREE
IS DECORATED FESTIVELY
WITH TINY DOTS OF COLORED LIGHT
THAT COZY UP THIS WINTER NIGHT.
CHRISTMAS SONGS, FAMILIAR, SLOW,
PLAY SOFTLY ON THE RADIO.
POPS AND HISSES FROM THE FIRE
WHISTLE WITH THE BELLS AND CHOIR.
MY TIGER IS NOW FAST ASLEEP
ON HIS BACK AND DREAMING DEEP.
WHEN THE FIRE MAKES HIM HOT,
HE TURNS TO WARM WHATEVER'S NOT.
PROPPED AGAINST HIM ON THE RUG,
I GIVE MY FRIEND A GENTLE HUG.
TOMORROW'S WHAT I'M WAITING FOR,
BUT I CAN WAIT A LITTLE MORE.
WATTERSON

HA HA! IT'S CHRISTMAS! HURRY UP, MOM AND DAD! IT'S ALMOST DAWN!
HERE, I GOT YOU A PRESENT.

YOU GOT ME A PRESENT? GOSH HOBBES, HOW NICE!
I PICKED IT OUT MYSELF! OPEN IT!

WHY, IT'S... IT'S THREE CANS OF... UH... SALMON. UM, THANKS, HOBBES.
YOU'RE WELCOME!

GEE, I DIDN'T GET YOU A PRESENT. I FEEL TERRIBLE.
I THOUGHT OF THAT. SEE, YOU COULD GIVE ME MINE BACK! THAT WOULD BE A GOOD PRESENT!

WELL THEN, HERE! MERRY CHRISTMAS, HOBBES!
WHY, THANK YOU! IT'S JUST WHAT I WANTED! MERRY CHRISTMAS!
CALVIN, DID YOU KNOCK THESE CANS OVER IN THE PANTRY?

WELL, HERE WE ARE, POISED AT THE PRECIPICE OF "PALLBEARER PEAK" ON A FLIMSY, UNSTEERABLE SLED!

THE MIND RECOILS IN HORROR TO IMAGINE THE AWFUL DESCENT! YES, IT'S A THOUSAND FOOT VERTICAL DROP ONTO A BOULDER FIELD LINED WITH PRICKER BUSHES! IT'S A JOURNEY CALCULATED TO EXCEED THE HUMAN CAPACITY FOR BLINDING FEAR!

READY TO GO?
READY!

NEW HAT, DAD?
YEP.

I LIKE IT.
THANK YOU. SO DO I.

AAUGH!
YOU'RE GOING TO BE LATE FOR WORK, DAD!

WATTERSON
YOU DON'T **LIKE** MY "SNOWMAN HOUSE OF HORROR," **DO** YOU?!

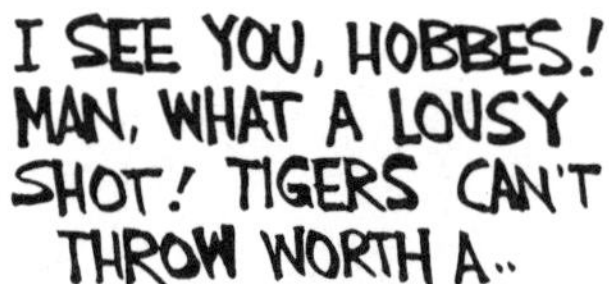
I SEE YOU, HOBBES! MAN, WHAT A LOUSY SHOT! TIGERS CAN'T THROW WORTH A..

SMACK!

I JUST THREW THE FIRST ONE SO YOU'D TURN AROUND.
WATTERSON

A NEW DECADE IS COMING UP.
YEAH, BIG DEAL! HMPH.

WHERE ARE THE FLYING CARS? WHERE ARE THE MOON COLONIES? WHERE ARE THE PERSONAL ROBOTS AND THE ZERO GRAVITY BOOTS, HUH? YOU CALL THIS A NEW DECADE?! YOU CALL THIS THE FUTURE?? **HA!**

WHERE ARE THE ROCKET PACKS? WHERE ARE THE DISINTEGRATION RAYS? WHERE ARE THE FLOATING CITIES?

FRANKLY, I'M NOT SURE PEOPLE HAVE THE BRAINS TO MANAGE THE TECHNOLOGY THEY'VE **GOT**.
I MEAN, **LOOK** AT THIS! WE STILL HAVE **WEATHER?!** GIVE ME A BREAK!
WATTERSON

Calvin and HOBBES
by WATTERSON
ARE YOUR PARENTS GOING OUT FOR NEW YEAR'S EVE?
ARE YOU KIDDING?

MY PARENTS' IDEA OF A WILD NIGHT IS TO MIX A SCOOP OF REAL COFFEE IN WITH THE DECAF.

ARE YOU MAKING ANY RESOLUTIONS FOR THE NEW YEAR?

RESOLUTIONS? ME?? JUST WHAT ARE YOU IMPLYING? THAT I NEED TO CHANGE?? WELL, BUDDY, AS FAR AS I'M CONCERNED, I'M PERFECT THE WAY I AM!

FOR YOUR INFORMATION, I'M STAYING LIKE THIS, AND EVERYONE ELSE CAN JUST GET USED TO IT! IF PEOPLE DON'T LIKE ME THE WAY I AM, WELL, TOUGH BEANS! IT'S A FREE COUNTRY! I DON'T NEED ANYONE'S PERMISSION TO BE THE WAY I WANT! THIS IS HOW I AM - TAKE IT OR LEAVE IT!

BY GOLLY, LIFE'S TOO DARN SHORT TO WASTE TIME TRYING TO PLEASE EVERY MEDDLESOME MORON WHO'S GOT AN IDEA HOW I OUGHT TO BE! I DON'T NEED ADVICE! EVERYONE CAN JUST STAY OUT OF MY FACE!

I...
..HOBBES?

HMPH!

HE SHOULD RESOLVE TO BE MORE ATTENTIVE WHEN SOMEONE IS SPEAKING.
WATTERSON

BEFORE GOING DOWN A STEEP HILL LIKE THIS, ONE SHOULD ALWAYS GIVE HIS SLED A SAFETY CHECK.
RIGHT.

SEAT BELTS?
NONE.
SIGNALS?
NONE.

BRAKES?
NONE.
STEERING?
NONE.

WHEEEEEE

HOW COLD IS IT OUTSIDE?
I DON'T KNOW. WHY DON'T YOU CHECK?

IT'S PRETTY DARN COLD, I'D SAY.
LET ME SHOW YOU AN INTERESTING GADGET THAT'S HANGING OUTSIDE THE WINDOW.

!!

THIS IS THE PART OF WINTER I LIKE BEST... WHEN YOU COME INSIDE, FREEZING COLD AND SOAKED...

...AND YOU PUT ON FRESH DRY CLOTHES, AND RUN UP TO THE WARM KITCHEN, WHERE MOM'S GOT A STEAMING MUG OF HOT CHOCOLATE WAITING FOR YOU!

MOM? ... MOM?? HEY MOM!

"CALVIN, I'M NEXT DOOR. DON'T HAVE ANYTHING TO EAT, OR YOU'LL SPOIL YOUR APPETITE. MOM."
IT'S GOING TO BE A LONG, COLD, DARK WINTER.

WHILE *I'M* DOING THIS BRAIN SURGERY, *YOU* CAN MAKE A DONOR AND DO A HEART TRANSPLANT!
FORGET IT, CALVIN. I'M NOT PLAYING WITH YOU ANY MORE.

Calvin and Hobbes

by WATTERSON

HEE HEE HEE HEE

BUT FOR MY OWN EXAMPLE, I'D NEVER BELIEVE ONE LITTLE KID COULD HAVE SO MUCH BRAINS!

I'M A GENIUS, HOBBES. THERE'S SIMPLY NO OTHER WORD FOR IT. WHO ELSE WOULD THINK TO ARM A TOBOGGAN? IT'S JUST GENIUS!

SEE SUSIE DERKINS DOWN THERE? SHE'S BUILDING A SNOWMAN AND DOESN'T EVEN KNOW WE'RE UP HERE! WE'LL ZIP DOWN AND PELT HER SILLY WITH SNOWBALLS!

YOU STEER AND I'LL THROW! SEE, THE SNOWBALLS WILL GAIN EVEN MORE FORCE FROM OUR OWN VELOCITY! GENIUS, HUH?

HA HA! WE'LL BE A MILE AWAY BEFORE SHE CAN EVEN PICK HER HEAD OUT OF THE SNOW!

THERE SHE IS! STEER CLOSER SO I CAN GET HER! LEAN! LEAN!

AUGH! STEER! YOU'RE TOO CLOSE! MAYDAY!!

PIFF!

ANOTHER GENIUS THWARTED BY AN INCAPABLE ASSISTANT.
HEY CALVIN, LOOK UP.

LOOK, HOBBES! MY NEWEST INVENTION!
ISN'T THAT YOUR TRANSMOGRIFIER?

IT WAS, BUT I MADE SOME MODIFICATIONS. SEE, THE BOX IS ON ITS SIDE NOW. IT'S A DUPLICATOR!
AH.

IT COMBINES THE TECHNOLOGIES OF THE TRANSMOGRIFIER AND A PHOTOCOPIER, SO INSTEAD OF MERELY MAKING A REPRODUCTION ON PAPER, THIS MACHINE ACTUALLY CREATES A REAL DUPLICATE!

SO OUR FINANCIAL WORRIES ARE OVER?
AND COUNTERFEITING IS JUST ONE OF ITS MANY USES AROUND THE HOME!
DUPLICATOR

HAVE YOU TESTED YOUR DUPLICATOR MACHINE YET?
I WAS JUST ABOUT TO. YOU CAN HELP.

OH BOY! WHAT WILL WE DUPLICATE FIRST?
ME!

YOU??
YEAH! MOM WANTS ME TO CLEAN MY ROOM, SO I'LL DUPLICATE MYSELF AND LET THE DUPLICATE DO THE WORK! SMART, HUH?

I CAN PICTURE THE LOOK ON YOUR PARENTS' FACES WHEN THEY FIND OUT THEY'VE SUDDENLY HAD TWINS.
TWINS, HECK! THIS SUMMER I CAN MAKE A WHOLE BASEBALL TEAM!

OK HOBBES, PRESS THE BUTTON AND DUPLICATE ME.
ARE YOU SURE THIS IS SUCH A GOOD IDEA?

BROTHER! YOU DOUBTING THOMASES GET IN THE WAY OF MORE SCIENTIFIC ADVANCES WITH YOUR STUPID ETHICAL QUESTIONS! THIS IS A BRILLIANT IDEA! HIT THE BUTTON, WILL YA?

I'D HATE TO BE ACCUSED OF INHIBITING SCIENTIFIC PROGRESS... HERE YOU GO.
BOINK
BUTTON

SCIENTIFIC PROGRESS GOES "BOINK"?
IT WORKED! IT WORKED! I'M A GENIUS!
NO YOU'RE NOT, YOU LIAR! I INVENTED THIS!

THE DUPLICATOR WORKED! HOBBES, MEET MY DUPLICATE!
OOG. I'M NOT SURE I'M READY FOR THIS.
HEY, NICE ROOM.

OK, DUPE! HOBBES AND I ARE GOING OUT TO PLAY. YOU CLEAN MY ROOM, AND WHEN YOU'RE DONE, I'VE GOT SOME HOMEWORK YOU CAN DO, TOO.
WHAT?!

FORGET IT, BUB! FIND SOME OTHER SUCKER TO DO YOUR DIRTY WORK! LAST ONE OUTSIDE IS A ROTTEN EGG!
HEY! COME BACK HERE!

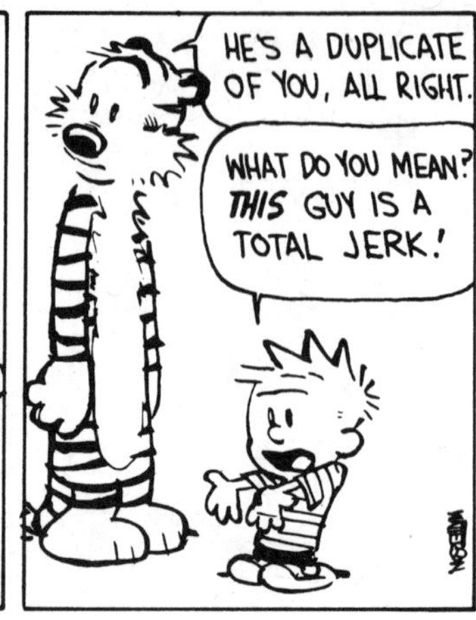
HE'S A DUPLICATE OF YOU, ALL RIGHT.
WHAT DO YOU MEAN? THIS GUY IS A TOTAL JERK!

WHERE ARE YOU GOING? DID YOU CLEAN YOUR ROOM LIKE I ASKED YOU TO?

I'M GOING OUTSIDE. CALVIN CAN CLEAN HIS OWN ROOM.
I DON'T WANT ANY NONSENSE, CALVIN. GO UPSTAIRS.

CALVIN? I'M NOT CALVIN. I'M HIS DUPLICATE. CALVIN'S IN HIS ROOM.
WHAT DID I JUST SAY? NO NONSENSE, CALVIN! GO CLEAN YOUR ROOM.

BOY, YOU ARE A CRABBY LADY! WHO ARE YOU? CALVIN'S CRUEL GOVERNESS?
THAT DOES IT.

C'MON, HOBBES. WE'D BETTER GO FIND MY DUPLICATE BEFORE HE GETS ME IN TROUBLE.

I'M TELLING YOU, LADY, YOU'VE GOT THE WRONG GUY! I'M A DUPLICATE OF CALVIN! CALVIN'S IN HIS ROOM!
WE'LL SEE ABOUT THAT. GIVE ME YOUR COAT.

SEE, CALVIN? THERE'S NO ONE HERE. NOW THAT'S ENOUGH GAMES. CLEAN YOUR ROOM, OK?
CALVIN?

I DON'T SEE HIM, HOBBES. MAYBE HE'S OUTSIDE, HUH?
WE'D BETTER HURRY. I THINK I HEAR YOUR MOM COMING DOWN THE STAIRS.

CALVIN! WHAT ARE YOU DOING OUTSIDE? DIDN'T I JUST SEND YOU TO CLEAN YOUR ROOM TWO MINUTES AGO?!
NO.

I DID TOO! NOW GET BACK UPSTAIRS. I'M LOSING MY PATIENCE FOR THIS GAME!
SHE MUST'VE FOUND MY DUPLICATE! C'MON HOBBES, WE'D BETTER HURRY BEFORE HE GETS US IN MORE TROUBLE!

NUMBER THREE, HI! I'M NUMBER TWO!
CHARMED.
DUPLI

MOM SAID SHE SENT ME UPSTAIRS A MINUTE AGO! THAT MUST'VE BEEN MY DUPLICATE!
WHAT A MESS THIS IS TURNING OUT TO BE!

YOU SAID IT! HE GETS IN TROUBLE, BUT I'M THE ONE WHO GETS BLAMED! WE'D BETTER STRAIGHTEN HIM...

AAUGH!

YOUR DUPLICATOR IS A BIG SUCCESS.
ARE YOU KIDDING? IT BURNED OUT AFTER THE FIFTH ONE OF US!
OH NO!

OH NO! MY DUPLICATE MADE DUPLICATES!
HI! WE'RE NUMBERS TWO THROUGH SIX!
HI!
HI!
HI!

HOBBES, WHAT AM I GOING TO DO?!
BETTER TELL YOUR MOM TO PUT OUT THE EXTRA TABLE SETTINGS.

LOOK, YOU GUYS HAVE TO STAY IN HERE AND BE REAL QUIET! IF MY MOM FINDS OUT ABOUT THIS, SHE'LL HAVE A FIT!
STAY HERE?!
NO WAY.
FORGET IT.

I'M THE ORIGINAL! YOU HAVE TO DO WHAT I SAY!
OH YEAH? LET'S PUT IT TO A VOTE.

I DON'T KNOW ABOUT THE REST OF YOU, BUT *I'M* GOING TO GET SOME COOKIES!
I'M GOING OUTSIDE!
I WONDER WHAT'S ON TV NOW?
YOU GUYS, COME BACK! MOM WILL *SEE* YOU!

SO WHAT? SO LONG AS WE SPLIT UP AND SHE ONLY SEES ONE OF US AT A TIME, SHE'LL JUST THINK WE'RE *YOU*!
HA
HA
HA, HA
HA

WHAT A BUNCH OF DEVIOUS LITTLE STINKERS! WHERE'D THEY LEARN TO MISBEHAVE LIKE THAT?!
I THINK WE SHOULD CHECK INTO A HOTEL UNTIL THIS IS OVER.

CALVIN, YOU KNOW YOU'RE NOT ALLOWED TO EAT COOKIES BEFORE DINNER! PUT THOSE AWAY! DID YOU CLEAN YOUR ROOM YET?

I'M NOT CALVIN. I'M A DUPLICATE.
I DON'T WANT TO HEAR ABOUT IT. NOW MOVE!

OOH, SOME DAYS THAT KID OF MINE...

WHAT ARE YOU DOING IN *HERE*?!
WHY? ARE YOU TAKING A SURVEY?

I'M HOME!
HI.

HI, CALVIN.

HI.
I *SAID* HI.

HI.
KNOCK IT OFF, CALVIN.
DEAR, HAVE A TALK WITH HIM. HE'S BEEN DRIVING ME CRAZY.

OK DUPLICATES, LISTEN UP. AS LONG AS YOU'RE ALL HERE AND I DON'T KNOW HOW TO GET RID OF YOU, WE MIGHT AS WELL COOPERATE.

SPECIFICALLY, WITH FIVE DUPLICATES, WE CAN DIVIDE UP THE SCHOOL WEEK SO THERE'S ONE DUPLICATE FOR EACH DAY.

IF THE REST OF US LAY LOW, WE CAN TAKE TURNS GOING TO SCHOOL, AND NO ONE WILL BE THE WISER!
GREAT!

NOW THAT STILL LEAVES US WITH THE QUESTION OF WHO GETS THE BED TONIGHT.
WE'LL FIGHT YOU FOR IT.

HI CALVIN.
I'M NOT CALVIN. I'M DUPLICATE NUMBER TWO.

WHAT ARE YOU TALKING ABOUT?
WE DREW STRAWS, AND TODAY'S MY DAY TO GO TO SCHOOL. WE'RE ALL TAKING TURNS SO WE EACH ONLY GO ONCE A WEEK.

CALVIN, YOU ARE SO WEIRD I'M NOT EVEN GOING TO TALK TO YOU.

I'M NOT CALVIN.

I WISH I LIVED SOME-PLACE WHERE I WENT TO A NORMAL BUS STOP.
ARE YOU IN CALVIN'S CLASS? WILL YOU HELP ME FIND HIS LOCKER?

CALVIN, WOULD YOU PLEASE DEMONSTRATE THE HOMEWORK PROBLEM YOU WERE ASSIGNED YESTERDAY?

I WASN'T HERE YESTERDAY.
YES, YOU WERE, CALVIN. DIDN'T YOU DO YOUR PROBLEM?

I'M NOT CALVIN. I'M DUPLICATE NUMBER FIVE. DUPLICATE ***TWO*** WAS HERE YESTERDAY, NOT ***ME***. WE'RE ALL TAKING TURNS. NUMBER TWO WILL BE BACK NEXT WEEK, AND YOU CAN ASK HIM TO DO THE PROBLEM ***THEN***.

LOOK, I DON'T SEE WHAT'S SO HARD ABOUT THIS!
PRINCIPAL

GUYS? IT'S OK TO COME OUT! IT'S ME, NUMBER FOUR. I'M HOME.

HOW WAS SCHOOL TODAY?
AHH, I GOT SENT TO THE PRINCIPAL'S OFFICE, JUST LIKE NUMBERS TWO AND FIVE DID.

GEEZ, YOU GUYS! EVEN **I** DON'T GET SENT TO THE PRINCIPAL EVERY **DAY**! YOU'RE MAKING ME LOOK BAD!
LOOK, CALVIN, IF YOU DON'T LIKE OUR PERFORMANCE, YOU CAN GO TO SCHOOL **YOURSELF**!

WHOA, LET'S NOT JUMP TO CONCLUSIONS! I'M JUST SAYING THERE'S ROOM FOR IMPROVEMENT.
HEY FOUR, WERE YOU ABLE TO SWIPE ANY CHALK?
YEAH! THE PRINCIPAL NEVER FRISKED ME!

HOBBES, WE'VE GOT TO GET RID OF THESE DUPLICATES! ALL THEY DO IS GET ME IN TROUBLE!

EVERYONE THINKS ***I'M*** DOING ALL THESE ROTTEN THINGS, WHEN REALLY IT'S A DUPLICATE! I'M BEING FRAMED BY MY OWN DOUBLES!

RUN!
HIDE!
OUTTA MY WAY!

IT APPEARS YOU'VE JUST PERPETRATED ANOTHER CRIME.
THE WORST PART IS THAT I DON'T EVEN HAVE THE FUN OF DOING THE STUFF I'M GETTING BLAMED FOR.

ALL RIGHT, WHAT DID YOU GUYS DO ***NOW***?
YOU'D BETTER HIDE, CALVIN! YOUR MOM'S ON THE WARPATH!

CALVIN?
SHE'S COMING! QUICK, GET UNDER THE DUPLICATOR BOX!
DUPLI

THERE YOU ARE! WHAT HAVE YOU GOT TO SAY FOR YOURSELF? I WANT AN EXPLANATION FOR THIS BEHAVIOR!
DUPLICATOR

TELL HER YOU NEED A BIGGER ALLOWANCE!
YEAH! FIVE ***TIMES*** BIGGER!
UM, CAN I GET BACK TO YOU ON THIS, MOM?
NO.

BOY, MOM SURE READ *ME* THE RIOT ACT, DIDN'T SHE?
I HAVE AN IDEA.

PSST, CALVIN! IS THE COAST CLEAR?
DID YOUR MOM GO AWAY YET?
CAN WE COME OUT NOW?

OH NO! YOUR MOM'S COMING BACK!
THERE SHE IS! STAY IN THE BOX, GUYS! KEEP QUIET!
YIKES!
SHH!

HOBBES, YOU'RE A GENIUS!
I DON'T HEAR HER. DO YOU?
HEY, WHAT'S GOING ON OUT THERE?
DUPLICATOR
TRANSMO
-RIFIER

SO LONG, DUPLICATES!
WHAT DO YOU MEAN? WE'RE NOT GOING ANYWH...
TRANSMOG
-RIFIER

ZAP!
DUPLICATOR
TRANSM
-RIFIE

WHAT DID YOU TRANSMOGRIFY THEM INTO?
WORMS!

WORMS?!
WELL, I DIDN'T WANT THEM TO BE UNHAPPY...
COOL! LOOK AT US!
HA HA! LET'S GO GROSS SOMEONE OUT!

WELL MOM, YOU DON'T NEED TO WORRY ABOUT ME GETTING IN TROUBLE ANY MORE.
OH REALLY?

YUP. SEE, I MADE THESE DUPLICATES OF MYSELF, AND *THEY* WERE THE ONES WHO WERE BAD, NOT ME.
UH HUH...

BUT *NOW* LOOK! I TRANSMOG-RIFIED THEM!
OH CALVIN! DON'T CARRY *WORMS* THROUGH THE HOUSE! OUT! OUT!

WELL THERE! YOU GOT ME IN TROUBLE ONE LAST TIME. I HOPE YOU'RE HAPPY!
YOU'RE SURE YOU DON'T WANT TO PUT US ON YOUR DAD'S DINNER PLATE TONIGHT BEFORE WE GO?

WELL, HOBBES, I GUESS WE LEARNED A VALUABLE LESSON FROM THIS DUPLICATING MESS.

AND THAT IS?
AND THAT IS, UM... IT'S THAT, WELL...

OK, SO WE DIDN'T LEARN ANY BIG LESSON. SUE ME.
LIVE AND DON'T LEARN, THAT'S US.

WHAP!

DID YOU THROW THAT?!?
THROW WHAT?

LET ME SEE YOUR MITTENS! THERE, LOOK! FLECKS OF BARK, PIECES OF GRAVEL, SPOTS OF MUD, AND GRANULES OF ICE! THAT WAS YOUR SNOWBALL, ALL RIGHT!

THAT'S THE PROBLEM WITH HAVING A SIGNATURE STYLE.

HA! YOU MISSED BY A MILE! NYAH NYAHH!
THBPTBH!

YES?
YOU'RE DARN LUCKY I DIDN'T GET THAT SNOW-BLOWER FOR CHRISTMAS!

Calvin and HOBBES
by WATTERSON

WATTERSON

Calvin and Hobbes
by Watterson
WHOSE BRILLIANT IDEA WAS IT TO TAKE A HIKE OUT IN THIS BITTER COLD?! HOW MUCH LONGER DO WE HAVE TO DO THIS?

I FEEL LIKE I'M IN "DR. ZHIVAGO."
ALL RIGHT, CALVIN. YOU'VE MADE YOUR POINT, I THINK.

I HATE THESE FORCED MARCHES! WHEN ARE WE GOING HOME?
THIS IS JUST A LITTLE WALK, CALVIN. THE EXERCISE IS GOOD FOR YOU.

BUT I'M FREEZING! IT MUST BE 80 BELOW! MY TOES ARE NUMB!
NUMB TOES BUILD CHARACTER.

YEAH? WELL, WHAT ABOUT FROSTBITE?! WHAT ABOUT HYPOTHERMIA?! WHAT ABOUT DEATH?! I SUPPOSE THOSE BUILD CHARACTER TOO! I CAN'T BELIEVE I'M OUT HERE!

THIS IS THE WORST DAY OF MY ENTIRE LIFE! I HATE THIS! AREN'T WE GOING HOME YET? IT SEEMS LIKE WE'VE BEEN WALKING FOR HOURS!
CALVIN, WILL YOU PLEASE STOP GRIPING?

GRIPING? I'M NOT GRIPING! I'M JUST OBSERVING WHAT A MISERABLE EXPERIENCE THIS IS! BUT OK! SURE! AS LONG AS I'M TRUDGING HUNDREDS OF MILES FOR NO APPARENT REASON, I MIGHT AS WELL DO IT IN SILENCE, RIGHT?!

JUST BECAUSE I'M OUT IN THE ELEMENTS LIKE A COMPLETE IDIOT, WATCHING MY DIGITS TURN TO ICE AND FALL OFF, I SURE AS HECK WOULDN'T EVER WANT TO SPOIL THE...
WE'RE HOME.

WE'RE WHAT? OH LOOK, WE'RE HOME!

WATTERSON

QUIZ:
Jack and Joe leave their homes at the same time and drive toward each other. Jack drives at 60 mph, while Joe drives at 30 mph. They pass each other in 10 minutes.

How far apart were Jack and Joe when they started?

IT WAS ANOTHER BAFFLING CASE. BUT THEN, YOU DON'T HIRE A **PRIVATE EYE** FOR THE **EASY** ONES...

I'D PLANNED TO TAKE THE DAY **OFF AND** SPEND TIME WITH A COUPLE OF **BUDDIES**. MY BUDDIES TRAVEL LIGHT AND THEY'RE FUN TO HAVE AROUND. ONE TRAVELS IN A HOLSTER, AND THE OTHER IN A HIP FLASK.
MY NAME IS **BULLET**. TRACER BULLET. WHAT PEOPLE **CALL** ME IS SOMETHING ELSE AGAIN. I'M A PRIVATE EYE. IT SAYS SO ON MY DOOR.
PRIVATE EYE

THE **LAST** THING I WANTED THIS MORNING WAS A **CASE** TO SOLVE, BUT THE DAME WHO BROUGHT IT WAS **PERSUASIVE**. MOST DAMES **ARE**, SOMEHOW.

GET TO WORK, CALVIN.
I TOLD HER IT WOULD COST HER FIFTY GREENBACKS A DAY, PLUS EXPENSES.

I STEPPED OUT INTO THE RAINY STREETS AND REVIEWED THE FACTS. THERE WEREN'T MANY.

TWO SAPS, JACK AND JOE, DRIVE TOWARD EACH OTHER AT 60 AND 30 MPH. AFTER 10 MINUTES, THEY PASS. I'M SUPPOSED TO FIND OUT HOW FAR APART THEY STARTED.

QUESTIONS POUR DOWN LIKE THE RAIN. WHO **ARE** THESE MUGS? WHAT WERE THEY TRYING TO ACCOMPLISH? WHY WAS JACK IN SUCH A HURRY? AND WHAT DIFFERENCE DOES IT MAKE WHERE THEY STARTED FROM?!

I HAD A HUNCH THAT, BEFORE THIS WAS OVER, I'D BE SORRY I ASKED.

FIRST I FIGURED I'D TRY THE DERKINS DAME. SUSIE AND I NEVER HIT IT OFF, ALTHOUGH OCCASIONALLY WE HIT EACH OTHER.

SUSIE HAD A FACE THAT SUGGESTED SOMEBODY UPSTAIRS HAD A WEIRD SENSE OF HUMOR, BUT I WASN'T GOING TO HER PLACE FOR LAUGHS. I NEEDED INFORMATION.

THE WAY *I* LOOKED AT IT, DERKINS ACTED AWFULLY SMUG FOR A DAME WHO HAD A HEAD FOR NUMBERS AND NOT MUCH ELSE. MAYBE SHE'S GOT SOMETHING ON JACK AND JOE. THE QUESTION IS, WILL SHE SING?

NO, I WON'T TELL YOU WHAT THE ANSWER IS! DO YOUR **OWN** WORK!

THE DERKINS DAME WASN'T TALKING. SOMEONE HAD GOTTEN TO HER FIRST AND SHUT HER UP GOOD. I KNEW SUSIE, AND CLOSING HER MOUTH WOULD'VE TAKEN SOME WORK.

I NEEDED A CLUE AND A DRINK. ONE OF THEM I KNEW WHERE TO FIND.

YOU'VE MADE ENOUGH TRIPS TO THE WATER FOUNTAIN. FINISH YOUR QUIZ.

SUDDENLY A GORILLA PULLED ME IN AN ALLEY, SQUEEZED MY SPINE INTO AN ACCORDION, AND PLAYED A POLKA ON ME WITH BRASS KNUCKLES!
YOUSE AIN'T GOIN' NOWHERE, FLATFOOT.

THE INSIDE OF MY HEAD WAS EXPLODING WITH FIREWORKS. FORTUNATELY, MY LAST THOUGHT TURNED OUT THE LIGHTS WHEN IT LEFT.

WHEN I CAME TO, THE PIECES ALL FIT TOGETHER. JACK AND JOE'S LIVES WERE DEFINED BY INTEGERS. OBVIOUSLY, THEY WERE PART OF A "NUMBERS" RACKET!

BACK IN THE OFFICE, I PULLED THE FILES ON ALL THE NUMBERS **BIG** ENOUGH TO KEEP SUSIE QUIET AND WANT ME OUT OF THE PICTURE. THE ANSWER HIT ME LIKE A .44 SLUG. IT HAD TO BE THE NUMBER THEY CALLED "MR. BILLION."

Answer: 1,000,000,000
TIME'S UP. BRING YOUR PAPERS FORWARD.
CASE CLOSED!
WHAT DID YOU GET, CALVIN? I THINK THE ANSWER'S 15.

Calvin and Hobbes by WATTERSON

I THINK THIS IS MY FAVORITE TIME OF YEAR! THE NEW SNOW MAKES EVERYTHING LOOK SO PRETTY.

WHOAAAAAA!
WUMPH!

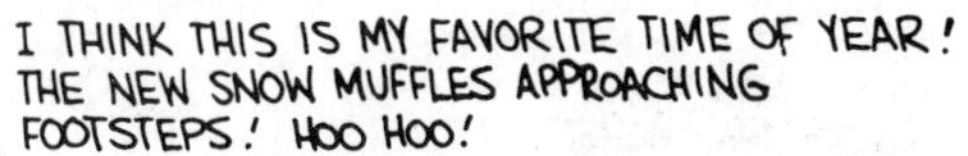
I THINK THIS IS MY FAVORITE TIME OF YEAR! THE NEW SNOW MUFFLES APPROACHING FOOTSTEPS! HOO HOO!

MAN, I CAN'T WAIT FOR SPRING.
WATTERSON

Calvin and HobbEs
by WATTERSON
LET'S HURRY DOWN THIS HILL AND GO HOME.

WHAT'S THE RUSH?
THERE'S A TV SHOW ON SLEDDING I WANT TO WATCH.

IN MY OPINION, TELEVISION VALIDATES EXISTENCE.

TAKE THIS SLED RIDE, FOR INSTANCE. THE EXPERIENCE IS FLEETING AND ELUSIVE. BY TOMORROW, WE'LL HAVE FORGOTTEN IT, AND IT MAY AS WELL HAVE NOT EVEN HAPPENED.

BUT IF WE WERE ON TV NOW, COUNTLESS VIEWERS WOULD SHARE IN THE EVENT AND CONFIRM IT! THIS RIDE WOULD BECOME A PART OF MASS CONSCIOUSNESS!

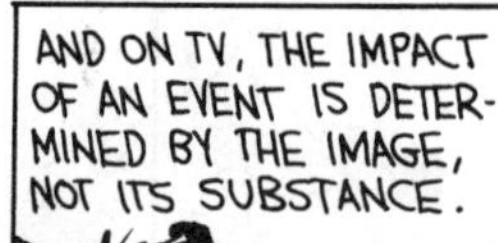
AND ON TV, THE IMPACT OF AN EVENT IS DETERMINED BY THE IMAGE, NOT ITS SUBSTANCE.

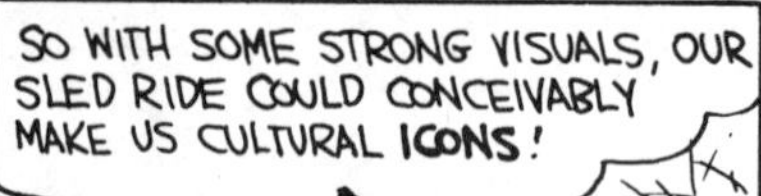
SO WITH SOME STRONG VISUALS, OUR SLED RIDE COULD CONCEIVABLY MAKE US CULTURAL **ICONS**!

INSTEAD OF BEING BORING OL' CALVIN AND HOBBES, WE'D BE "CALVIN AND HOBBES-***AS SEEN ON TV***"! WOULDN'T THAT BE GREAT? DON'T YOU WISH WE WERE ON TV?

AT THIS MOMENT, I LIKE MY ANONYMITY.

I THINK WE SHOULD GO FOR THE HIGH-BROW PUBLIC TV AUDIENCE, DON'T YOU?
WATTERSON

I MISSED THE BUS, MOM.
OH NO.

HURRY! IF WE JUMP IN THE CAR, YOU CAN ZOOM UP, PASS THE BUS ON A STRAIGHTAWAY, DROP ME OFF AT A LATER STOP, AND I CAN RIDE THE BUS FROM THERE!

C'MON! WHAT ARE YOU WAITING FOR? REV UP THE CAR!

MOM'S SO LAZY.

READYYY... AIMMM....

BEDTIME, KIDDO.
AW, MOM! CAN'T I WATCH THE NEXT PROGRAM?

NO, YOU NEED YOUR SLEEP. C'MON.
CAN I JUST WATCH ANOTHER 15 MINUTES? PLEASE?? OK, JUST 10 MINUTES! THEN I'LL GO STRAIGHT TO BED! FIVE MINUTES! JUST FIVE MINUTES, OK?

TURN OFF THE TV.
LOOK, I'LL JUST WATCH A FEW MORE COMMERCIALS, OK? SEE, HERE'S MY FAVORITE GUM COMMERCIAL!

I GUESS THAT GOT PRETTY PATHETIC.

Calvin and Hobbes

by Watterson

OH NO! I JUST REMEMBERED THAT TODAY IS "SHOW AND TELL" DAY! I NEED SOMETHING TO SHOW AND TELL ABOUT!
CHOCOLATE FROSTED SUGAR BOMBS

WHY CAN'T YOU THINK OF THESE THINGS MORE THAN TWO MINUTES BEFORE THE BUS COMES?
WHAT CAN I TAKE? I'VE GOTTA TAKE SOMETHING!

I'VE.. AH..
ACHOOO

NEVER MIND, MOM! DO WE HAVE ANY PLASTIC BAGS?
I DON'T WANT TO KNOW. I DON'T WANT TO KNOW. I DON'T..

SEE? SEE? STARBOARD IS RIGHT! PORT IS LEFT!
OK, SO I WAS WRONG FOR ONCE IN MY LIFE! SHUT UP.

AARGHH! I MISSED! IT'S THESE DARN FUZZY MITTENS! THE SNOW STICKS TO 'EM AND YOU CAN'T THROW STRAIGHT! DARN IT! DARN IT! DARN IT!

I HATE THESE FUZZY MITTENS! IF ONLY MOM HAD GOTTEN ME PADDED GLOVES INSTEAD OF THESE NO-GOOD, AWFUL, ROTTEN FUZZY MITTENS!

WHAP!

WELL I'LL BE! MY FUZZY MITTENS HAVE PADS!

CALVIN and HOBBES
by WATTERSON
THE INCREDIBLE SPACEMAN SPIFF, INTERPLANETARY EXPLORER EXTRAORDINAIRE, DESCENDS TOWARD AN ALIEN PLANET SURFACE!

ANOTHER DAY, ANOTHER MIND-BOGGLING ADVENTURE!

THE FEARLESS SPACEMAN SPIFF CRUISES LOW OVER PLANET QUORG, A DESOLATE WORLD OF DEEP GORGES AND CANYONS!

SEARCHING FOR LIFE, OUR HERO EXPLORES THE PECULIAR ROCK FORMATIONS!

...THE VERY PECULIAR ROCK FORMATIONS! ...A LITTLE TOO PECULIAR, PERHAPS!

SUDDENLY OUR HERO REALIZES THAT THIS LANDSCAPE WAS NOT CREATED BY GEOLOGICAL FORCES! SPIFF HITS THE THRUSTERS!

WHILE SPIFF WAS SEARCHING FOR ALIEN LIFE, IT SEEMS ALIEN LIFE WAS SEARCHING FOR SPIFF! NO DOUBT IT WANTED THE EARTHLING FOR DINNER!

CALVIN, WHERE ARE YOU?! IT'S TIME FOR DINNER!
UGHH! SPIFF BLASTS INTO HYPERSPACE!
WATTERSON

WUMP!

ANY DUMB KID CAN BUILD A SNOWMAN, BUT IT TAKES A GENIUS LIKE ME TO CREATE ART.

THIS SNOW SCULPTURE TRANSCENDS CORPOREAL LIKENESS TO EXPRESS DEEPER TRUTHS ABOUT THE HUMAN CONDITION! THIS SCULPTURE IS ABOUT GRIEF AND SUFFERING!

ONE LOOK AT THE TORTURED COUNTENANCE OF THIS FIGURE CONFIRMS THAT THE ARTIST HAS DRUNK DEEPLY FROM THE CUP OF LIFE! THIS WORK SHALL ENDURE AND INSPIRE FUTURE GENERATIONS!

STILL MAKING SNOW ART?
YEP!

YESTERDAY YOUR SCULPTURE MELTED.
THIS TIME I'M TAKING ADVANTAGE OF MY MEDIUM'S IMPERMANENCE.

THIS SCULPTURE IS ABOUT TRANSIENCE. AS THIS FIGURE MELTS, IT INVITES THE VIEWER TO CONTEMPLATE THE EVANESCENCE OF LIFE. THIS PIECE SPEAKS TO THE HORROR OF OUR OWN MORTALITY!

HEY STUPID! IT'S TOO WARM TO BUILD A SNOWMAN! WHAT A DOPE! HA HA HA HA!
A PHILISTINE ON THE SIDEWALK.
GENIUS IS NEVER UNDERSTOOD IN ITS OWN TIME.

HOW'S YOUR SNOW ART PROGRESSING?
I'VE MOVED INTO ABSTRACTION!

AH.
THIS PIECE IS ABOUT THE INADEQUACY OF TRADITIONAL IMAGERY AND SYMBOLS TO CONVEY MEANING IN TODAY'S WORLD.

BY ABANDONING REPRESENTATIONALISM, I'M FREE TO EXPRESS MYSELF WITH PURE FORM. SPECIFIC INTERPRETATION GIVES WAY TO A MORE VISCERAL RESPONSE.

I NOTICE YOUR OEUVRE IS MONOCHROMATIC.
WELL C'MON, IT'S JUST SNOW.

DAD, IF YOU THREW A SNOWBALL AT SOMEONE, BUT DELIBERATELY MISSED, WOULD THAT BE "BAD"?

WELL, I SUPPOSE THAT WOULD BE PROVOKING, SO YES, IT WOULD BE A LITTLE BAD.
AS BAD AS IF YOU'D HIT THE PERSON?

NO, NOT THAT BAD, BUT WORSE THAN IF YOU HADN'T THROWN IT AT ALL.
SUPPOSE YOU JUST GRAZED THE PERSON. HOW BAD WOULD THAT BE?

SAY MAYBE YOU KNOCKED OFF HIS HAT AND HIS GLASSES OR SOMETHING.
THAT WOULD MEAN INSTANT DEATH.

BOY, THIS PUDDING WAS GREAT! CAN I TAKE A BOWL UPSTAIRS TO HOBBES?
NO, I THINK YOU'VE HAD ENOUGH.

I DIDN'T SAY FOR ME. I SAID FOR HOBBES!
WELL, I DON'T THINK "HOBBES" NEEDS ANY EITHER.

WHY NOT?!
UM... BECAUSE TIGERS NEED TO STAY LEAN AND MEAN.

THAT'S WHAT SHE SAID.
I'M LEAN! I'M MEAN! TELL HER CHOCOLATE PUDDING MAKES MY COAT LUSTROUS.

Calvin and HOBBES
by WATTERSON

S SSSSS
S SSSSS

IF THERE'S MORE TO LIFE THAN THIS, I DON'T KNOW WHAT IT IS.
WATTERSON

WHY SHOULD I GO TO SCHOOL?! WHY CAN'T I STAY HOME?

WHY DO I HAVE TO LEARN? WHY CAN'T I STAY THE WAY I AM? WHAT'S THE POINT OF THIS? WHY DO THINGS HAVE TO BE THIS WAY? WHY CAN'T THINGS BE DIFFERENT?

LIFE IS FULL OF MYSTERIES, ISN'T IT? SEE YOU THIS AFTERNOON.

AT 7:00 AM, MOM'S NOT VERY PHILOSOPHICAL.
WATERSON

ALL SET?
YEP!

OK, GET READY!

NOW!
CLICK
SMASH

TOO BAD THE BACK OF THE CAMERA OPENED WHEN WE LANDED. THAT WOULD'VE BEEN A GREAT PICTURE!
WATERSON

HA! I'VE GOT A GREAT WORD AND IT'S ON A "DOUBLE WORD SCORE" BOX!

"ZQFMGB" ISN'T A WORD! IT DOESN'T EVEN HAVE A VOWEL!
IT IS **SO** A WORD! IT'S A WORM FOUND IN NEW GUINEA! EVERYONE KNOWS THAT!

I'M LOOKING IT UP.
YOU DO, AND I'LL LOOK UP THAT 12-LETTER WORD **YOU** PLAYED WITH ALL THE Xs AND Js!

WHAT'S YOUR SCORE FOR ZQFMGB?
957.
WATERSON

HEY, NO TV UNTIL YOUR HOMEWORK IS DONE.
IT'S GETTING DONE.

NOT WITH YOU SITTING HERE, IT ISN'T.
HOBBES IS READING MY BOOK FOR ME.

AFTER I'M DONE WATCHING TV, HE'LL TELL ME WHAT THE BOOK WAS ABOUT, AND I'LL TELL HIM WHAT THE TV SHOWS WERE ABOUT! SEE, WE'RE DOING TWICE AS MUCH IN THE SAME AMOUNT OF TIME!

MOM SAYS YOU SHOULD WATCH TV AND I SHOULD READ THE DUMB BOOK.
UGH, I ONLY LIKE NATURE DOCUMENTARIES.

Hey Twinky, gimme a quarter.

WHAT?! WHY SHOULD I GIVE YOU MY MONEY?!

It's for the "Let Calvin Live Through Recess Fund."
SOUNDS LIKE A WORTHY CAUSE.

HIS MOTTO IS "GIVE BEFORE IT HURTS."

MOMMM! I NEED A DRINK OF WATER!

MPHHH... CALVIN, IT'S AFTER MIDNIGHT. GET A DRINK YOURSELF.
I CAN'T. THERE ARE MONSTERS UNDER MY BED! I'M SCARED.

OK... OK... OK...

AAUGH

Calvin and HOBBES
by WATTERSON

140 MILLION YEARS AGO, THE INCREDIBLE 'ULTRASAURS' WANDER THE EARTH! SOME WEIGH OVER 70 TONS, AND EVEN THE VICIOUS ALLOSAURS ARE NO MATCH FOR THESE GIANTS!

BUT WAIT! A DISTANT RUMBLING SENDS THE ULTRASAURS INTO A PANICKED STAMPEDE! IS IT A VOLCANO? IS IT AN EARTHQUAKE?

NO! IT'S.. IT'S A CALVINOSAURUS!

NAMED AFTER THE RENOWNED PALEONTOLOGIST WHO DISCOVERED IT, THE HUGE CALVINOSAUR CAN EAT AN ULTRASAUR IN A SINGLE BITE!

PHOOEY! I NEVER FIND ANYTHING.
IT LOOKS LIKE YOU'VE HIT THE SEWER PIPE.
WATTERSON

OK HOBBES, TOSS UP THIS DECK OF CARDS, AND I'LL PLUG THE ACE OF SPADES!
OH BOY, A SHOOTING TRICK!

GO!
BLAM BAM POW ZING BLOOIE BANG

HERE IT IS! WOW! SIX CLEAN HOLES THROUGH THE ACE!
PRETTY GOOD, HUH? WANT TO KNOW HOW I DID IT? I USED A HOLE PUNCHER AHEAD OF TIME!

HMM, ON SECOND THOUGHT, I'LL FOLD.
HEY, WHAT'S WITH THIS DECK?!

THIS MORNING I HAD A WONDERFUL DREAM. BY HOLDING MY ARMS OUT STIFF AND PUSHING DOWN HARD, I FOUND I COULD SUSPEND MYSELF A FEW FEET ABOVE THE GROUND. I FLAPPED HARDER, AND SOON I WAS SOARING EFFORTLESSLY OVER THE TREES AND TELEPHONE POLES! I COULD FLY! I FOLDED MY ARMS BACK AND ZOOMED LOW OVER THE NEIGHBORHOOD. EVERYONE WAS AMAZED, AND THEY RAN ALONG UNDER ME AS I SHOT BY. THEN I ROCKETED UP SO FAST THAT MY EYES WATERED FROM THE WIND. I LAUGHED AND LAUGHED, MAKING HUGE LOOPS ACROSS THE SKY! ...THAT'S WHEN MOM WOKE ME UP AND SAID I WAS GOING TO MISS THE BUS IF I DIDN'T GET MY BOTTOM OUT OF BED; 20 MINUTES LATER, HERE I AM, STANDING IN THE COLD RAIN, WAITING TO GO TO SCHOOL, AND I JUST REMEMBERED I FORGOT MY LUNCH.

TUESDAYS DON'T START MUCH WORSE THAN THIS.

I DID IT! I DID IT!

SOMEHOW I IMAGINED THIS EXPERIENCE WOULD BE MORE REWARDING.

HEWWO! IS HOBBESIE-WOBBSIE SWEEPY? OOH, HE'S JUST A BIG SNOOGIE-WOOGIE, ISN'T HE? YES HE *IS!* HEWWO, SNOOGIE-WOOGIE!

GLOMP!
HEY! HEY!

OW! LEGGO, YOU BLOODTHIRSTY CARNIVORE!
OW!
OW!
OW!

I CAN SEE WHY LITTLE TABBY CATS ARE SO MUCH MORE POPULAR.

ONCE UPON A TIME, THERE WAS A...
HOLD IT.

YOU KNOW WHAT *I'D* LIKE TO SEE? I'D LIKE TO SEE THE THREE BEARS EAT THE THREE LITTLE PIGS, AND THEN THE BEARS JOIN UP WITH THE BIG BAD WOLF AND EAT GOLDILOCKS AND LITTLE RED RIDING HOOD!

TELL ME A STORY LIKE *THAT*, OK?

AND HOW SHOULD HANSEL AND GRETEL MEET *THEIR* UNTIMELY DEMISE?
THE WITCH EATS THEM AND THEN THE WOLF EATS THE WITCH.

HEY DAD, CAN I TAKE THE GAS CAN FOR THE LAWN MOWER OUT IN THE BACK YARD?

WHAT ON EARTH FOR? IT'S 8:00 AT NIGHT!
I WANT TO POUR GASOLINE IN BIG LETTERS ON THE LAWN...

..AND SET FIRE TO IT SO AIRPLANES CAN READ IT AS THEY FLY OVER!
NO, YOU CAN'T DO THAT! DON'T BE RIDICULOUS!

I DON'T EVEN WANT TO KNOW WHAT HE INTENDED TO WRITE.

Calvin and HOBBES
by WATTERSON
BEWARE! FALLING BUCKEYES

HERE COMES SOMEBODY!

THIS MEETING OF THE TOP SECRET CLUB G.R.O.S.S. (GET RID OF SLIMY GIRLS) WILL COME TO ORDER. TODAY THIS AUGUST ASSEMBLY WILL DECIDE WHETHER TO DEMOTE PRESIDENT HOBBES ON CHARGES OF HERESY!
HERESY?!

LET THE RECORD SHOW THAT THE DEFENDANT MADE AN UNDISPARAGING COMMENT ABOUT THE POSSIBLE MEMBERSHIP OF SUSIE DERKINS, AN ADMITTED GIRL AND ENEMY OF THIS CLUB.

LET THE RECORD ALSO SHOW THAT SUPREME DICTATOR-FOR-LIFE CALVIN IS A NINCOMPOOP.
OK, JUST FOR THAT, YOU'RE ALSO CHARGED WITH INSUBORDINATION! THIS COURT FINDS YOU GUILTY ON BOTH COUNTS AND STRIPS YOU OF YOUR TITLE!

HA! AS COURT STENOGRAPHER, I REFUSE TO ENTER THE VERDICT! IN FACT, I'M PROMOTING MYSELF TO "EL TIGRE NUMERO UNO"!
OH YEAH?! WELL THEN, I PROMOTE MYSELF TO "MOST HIGHEST, GRANDEST, EXALTED, UM, SUPREME, UH..

THERE! I WROTE "HOBBES EQUALS GREAT" IN THE OFFICIAL CLUB NOTEBOOK! NOW IT'S A LAW!
IT IS NOT! GIMME THAT!
HOBS = GRAT

HA HA HA! I'M WRITING "HOBBES EQUALS UGLY FUR BALL"! WHAT DO YOU THINK OF THAT?
OH HO! I TAKE THE SUPREME DICTATOR HAT! NOW I'M THE SUPREME DICTATOR!

YOU GIVE THAT BACK!
I DECLARE YOU NULL AND VOID!

TRUCE?
TRUCE.

WHAT A GREAT CLUB. TOO BAD WE DON'T HAVE MORE MEMBERS.
MAYBE WE SHOULD ALLOW SUSIE TO JOIN.

DO YOU... I MEAN, DOES HOBBES WANT ANY TUNA FISH THIS WEEK?

NO, HOBBES STOPPED EATING CANNED TUNA. YOU KNOW, THEY KILL DOLPHINS TO GET IT.
OK, I'LL PUT IT BACK.

SO WHAT DOES HOBBES LIKE NOW INSTEAD?

FRESH SWORDFISH STEAKS. HE LIKES THEM GRILLED OUTSIDE.
MM-HMM. HOW ABOUT PEANUT BUTTER?

HERE'S SOME CLEAN CLOTHES. WILL YOU PUT THEM AWAY PLEASE?

HEY, MY UNDERWEAR ISN'T PRESSED! NEITHER ARE MY SOCKS! YOU DIDN'T FINISH IRONING!

BUDDY, IF YOU WANT YOUR UNDERWEAR IRONED, YOU CAN DO IT YOURSELF!
WHAT KIND OF MOTHER ARE YOU?!

SHE SHOULD TAKE MORE PRIDE IN HER WORK.

I ASKED MOM IF I WAS A GIFTED CHILD. ...SHE SAID THEY CERTAINLY WOULDN'T HAVE PAID FOR ME.

YOU CAN RELATE THIS LITTLE STORY WHEN THE REPORTERS ASK HOW I WENT BAD.

MOM! HOBBES IS READING MY COMIC BOOKS! TELL HIM TO STOP!

I TOLD HIM TO GO BUY HIS OWN, AND HE **SNARLED** AT ME! MAKE HIM GIVE 'EM BACK!
MAYBE YOU SHOULD BE GLAD HE'S MORE LITERATE THAN MOST STUFFED ANIMALS.

BUT THEY'RE **MY** COMIC BOOKS, NOT **HIS**!
WELL, YOU SHOULD LEARN TO SHARE. I DON'T THINK HOBBES WILL HURT THEM.

ARE YOU KIDDING?! HE DREW A MUSTACHE AND GLASSES ON EVERY PICTURE OF NUKE-MAN LAST ISSUE! IN **PEN**!
WHY DON'T YOU GO PLAY OUTSIDE, CALVIN.

HOW'S YOUR MATH COMING?

I DON'T **DO** MATH ANY MORE. I DECIDED I'M MORE OF A "VISUAL" PERSON.

GOOD. VISUALIZE BEING THE ONLY 45-YEAR-OLD IN FIRST GRADE.

VISUALIZING A FEW SUMS NOW, EH?
ACTUALLY, I'M VISUALIZING **YOU** IN TRACTION. HELP ME DO THESE, OK?

HEY HOBBES, I'LL GIVE YOU 20 QUESTIONS TO GUESS WHAT I HAVE IN MY HANDS, OK?
OK. IS IT LOATHSOME?
YES!
IS IT SOME BIG CENTIPEDE WITH POISON PINCHERS?
CENTIPEDES HAVE POISON PINCHERS?
I THINK SO.
MAN, IT'S A GOOD THING YOU GUESSED IT SO FAST!
WITH YOU, IT'S NEVER TOO DIFFICULT.

Calvin and HOBBES

by WATTERSON

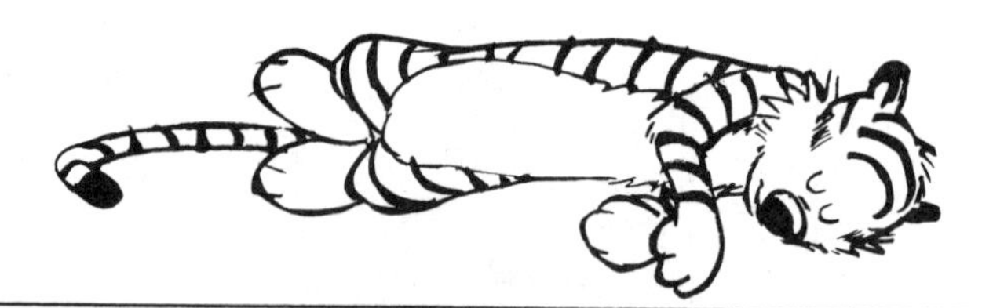

WHERE DO WE KEEP THE EXTENSION CORDS?
IN THE PANTRY, ON THE BOTTOM SHELF.

WHERE DO WE KEEP THE BLADES FOR DAD'S ELECTRIC SAW?
IN THE... WHY DO YOU WANT TO KNOW?

HUH? OH, I'M JUST MAKING AN INVENTORY LIST SO WE'LL ALWAYS KNOW WHERE TO FIND THINGS.

I GET THE FEELING THERE WAS NO RIGHT ANSWER TO THAT QUESTION.

CALVIN, COME OUT FROM WHEREVER YOU'RE HIDING AND TAKE YOUR BATH!

DO YOU HEAR ME, CALVIN?! I MEAN NOW!

OH NO! LOOK AT YOU! AUGH! GET OFF THE RUG!

LIKE IT'S MY FAULT SHE HASN'T GOTTEN THE CHIMNEY SWEPT.

MOM! MOM! I JUST SAW THE FIRST ROBIN OF SPRING! CALL THE NEWSPAPER QUICK!
HA HA! A FRONT PAGE WRITE-UP! A COMMEMORATIVE PLAQUE! A CIVIC CEREMONY! ALL FOR ME! HOORAY! HOORAY!
OH BOY! SHOULD I PUT THE PRIZE MONEY IN A TRUST FUND, OR BLOW IT ALL AT ONCE? HA HA! I CAN'T BELIEVE I DID IT!
CALVIN...

IT'S A HARD, BITTER, CRUEL WORLD TO HAVE TO GROW UP IN, HOBBES.
CHEER UP! DID I TELL YOU I SAW A ROBIN YESTERDAY?

I SURE LIKE CHOCOLATE FROSTED SUGAR BOMBS! LOOK HOW BROWN THE MILK GETS!
UGH.
MILK

WANT TO SEE SOMETHING WEIRD? LOOK AT THE NUTRITIONAL INFORMATION ON THE BACK PANEL.

WOW. 100% OF THE DAILY RECOMMENDED ALLOWANCE OF CAFFEINE!
HEY LOOK! YOU CAN SEND AWAY FOR A CHOCOLATE FROSTED SUGAR BOMBS "BUZZY THE HUMMINGBIRD" DOLL!

EENIE, MEENIE, MINEY, MOE! CATCH A TIGER BY THE TOE!
!

IF HE HOLLERS, UM... UH... ..HEH HEH...

WHO WRITES THESE DUMB THINGS ANYWAY?

COUNTY LIBRARY? YES, DO YOU HAVE ANY BOOKS ON HOMEMADE BOMBS?

THAT'S WHAT I SAID. I NEED A BOOK THAT LISTS SUPPLIES AND GIVES STEP-BY-STEP INSTRUCTIONS FOR BUILDING, RIGGING, AND DETONATING THEM.

WELL WHAT ABOUT YOUR OTHER BRANCHES? DON'T *THEY* HAVE ANY BOOKS LIKE THAT?

BOY, AND PEOPLE WONDER WHY KIDS DON'T READ.

Calvin and HOBBES
by WATTERSON

ISN'T THIS A NICE WAY TO SPEND THE EVENING? WE SHOULD DO THIS MORE OFTEN.

I STILL THINK ONE OF YOU BROKE THE RABBIT EARS ON PURPOSE.

IT'S GETTING LATE, CALVIN. YOU'D BETTER HEAD UP TO BED.
BUT I'M NOT TIRED! CAN'T I READ A LITTLE MORE?

I DON'T THINK SO. YOU SEE, WE DON'T WANT YOU TO GET TOO SMART.
YOU DON'T?
HA HA! OF COURSE NOT! IF YOU WERE SMARTER, YOU MIGHT REALIZE..

..YOUR "PARENTS" ARE REALLY BUG-EYED ALIENS FROM NEPTUNE!
HA
HA
HA
AUGH!

LET ME GO! LET ME GO!
GOT THE BATTER READY?
YEP! LET'S DUNK THE KID!

M-MM! THERE'S NOTHING LIKE A FRESH BATCH OF EARTH BOY WAFFLES!
WAFFLES? HELP! HELP!

EEP!
POOF

I WASN'T ASLEEP! I'M NOT TIRED!
WATTERSON

LOOK, HIS FACE WAS PUSHED INTO YOUR LEG SO HARD, IT LEFT CORDUROY LINES!
Z

I'M FREE! I'M FREE!

AT LAST! HOME SWEET HO...

OH NO.

HOO HOO! THAT WAS A GOOD ONE! LOOK HOW FAR WE LANDED!
A HOUSE WITH A TIGER IS NEVER A HOME.

LOOK AT YOU! HOW COULD ANYONE GET SO DIRTY AT SCHOOL?
I GOT THIS DIRTY JUST TRYING TO WALK IN THE FRONT DOOR! OL' CATAPULT BUTT WAS LYING IN WAIT FOR ME.

WELL, IT DOESN'T MATTER. YOU'D BETTER GET IN THE TUB NOW ANYWAY.
A BATH?!
BUT IT'S THE MIDDLE OF THE AFTERNOON!

YES, BUT I HAVE TO GET IN THE SHOWER BEFORE YOUR DAD GETS HOME, SO HE CAN TAKE ONE.
WHY ALL THE BATHS? IS THERE SOME EPIDEMIC GOING AROUND?

I TOLD YOU THIS MORNING WE'RE GOING OUT TONIGHT. ROSALYN WILL BE HERE AT 6:00.
AUGHHHH!

AAAAUUUUUUUUUGGGGGGGHHHHHHHHHHH!
LOOK, I KNOW YOU DON'T LIKE ROSALYN, BUT SHE'S THE ONLY BABY SITTER I COULD GET.

AND YOU REMEMBER OUR TALK AFTER WHAT HAPPENED LAST TIME, DON'T YOU? I WANT YOU ON YOUR BEST BEHAVIOR TONIGHT.

YOU DO EXACTLY WHAT SHE TELLS YOU. I DON'T WANT TO COME HOME AND HEAR ANY HORROR STORIES, OK?

FOR GOODNESS SAKE, CALVIN! TAKE A BREATH BEFORE YOU PASS OUT ON THE FLOOR!

WHAT ARE WE GOING TO DO, HOBBES? ROSALYN WILL BE HERE IN JUST A FEW HOURS!
DO YOU THINK SHE'LL REMEMBER HOW YOU LOCKED HER OUTSIDE LAST TIME?

IF SHE DOES, WE'RE DEAD! SHE'LL PROBABLY STICK MY HEAD ON A STAKE IN THE FRONT YARD AS A WARNING TO OTHER KIDS SHE BABY-SITS!
I'M ALMOST SURE THAT WOULD VIOLATE SOME ZONING ORDINANCE.

WELL NO MATTER WHAT, WE'RE IN BIG TROUBLE UNLESS WE THINK OF SOMETHING FAST!
I SUPPOSE WE COULD TRY BEING GOOD.

I MUST'VE GOTTEN WATER IN MY EAR. WHAT DID YOU SAY?
NOTHING. FORGET IT.

HI ROSALYN, COME ON IN. THANKS FOR COMING AGAIN.
NO TROUBLE.

HI ROSALYN! YOU DON'T NEED TO WORRY THIS TIME. CALVIN WILL BE ON HIS BEST BEHAVIOR TONIGHT.
EVEN SO, I'D LIKE AN ADVANCE.

AN ADVANCE? BUT... BUT...
DEAR, MAY I SPEAK WITH YOU A MOMENT?

BUT WE GAVE HER AN ADVANCE ON TONIGHT WHEN SHE LEFT LAST TIME!
I DON'T CARE. JUST PAY WHAT IT TAKES TO GET US OUT OF HERE!

OK, WE'RE GOING. ...AND CALVIN?
YES?

GCKKHHK!

I THINK I'LL SIT IN THE MIDDLE OF THE FLOOR AND LOOK AT THE WALL TONIGHT.
GOOD. I'LL TELL YOU WHEN IT'S BEDTIME.

THIS IS AWFUL! IF WE STEP OUT OF LINE **ONCE** TONIGHT, ROSALYN WILL KILL US, AND THEN MOM AND DAD WILL KILL US AGAIN WHEN THEY GET HOME.

I GUESS THAT'S THAT.
WHAT?! ADMIT DEFEAT? **NEVER!**

THINGS MAY LOOK GRIM FOR **US**, BUT **NOTHING** IS GRIM FOR...

...**STUPENDOUS MAN!** CHAMPION OF LIBERTY! FOE OF TYRANNY!
I'M GOING TO GET IN BED NOW AND AVOID THE RUSH.

A BOLT OF FIERY CRIMSON STREAKS ACROSS THE SKY! IT'S **STUPENDOUS MAN!**

THE FIENDISH **BABY SITTER GIRL** HAS A LOCAL HOUSEHOLD IN HER IRON GRIP OF TERROR! THE MAN OF MEGA-MIGHT ZOOMS TO THE RESCUE!

I'M IN LUCK! BABY SITTER GIRL IS MOMENTARILY DISTRACTED!

HI CHARLIE, IT'S ROSALYN. YEAH, I'M OVER AT THE LITTLE MONSTER'S HOUSE AGAIN. HMM? NO, ACTUALLY HE'S BEEN PRETTY GOOD TONIGHT. YEAH, I CAN'T BELIEVE IT.

ANYWAY CHARLIE, I'M SORRY WE COULDN'T GO OUT TONIGHT, BUT THIS LITTLE CREEP'S PARENTS ARE SO DESPERATE TO GET AWAY FROM HIM ONCE IN A WHILE THAT THEY...

YAHH! FREEDOM AND JUSTICE SHALL ALWAYS PREVAIL OVER TYRANNY, BABY SITTER GIRL!
!?!

GET OFF ME, CALVIN, YOU PEST! OW! LET GO! QUIT IT!
STUPENDOUS MAN HAS THE STRENGTH OF A MILLION MORTAL MEN! GIVE UP!

LISTEN CHARLIE, I'M GOING TO HAVE TO CALL YOU BACK. YOU WOULDN'T BELIEVE WHAT THIS CRETIN IS WEARING.
WITH MUSCLES OF MAGNITUDE, **STUPENDOUS MAN** FIGHTS WITH HEROIC RESOLVE!

SEE, IF WE HAD BOUGHT A DOG INSTEAD, LIKE I WANTED, WE COULD GO OUT LIKE THIS ALL THE TIME.
HONEY, WE CAME HERE TO RELAX. LET'S TALK ABOUT SOMETHING ELSE.

THERE GOES ROSALYN AROUND THE HOUSE AGAIN. SHE STILL DOESN'T KNOW YOU SNEAKED BACK INSIDE.
NOW I'LL CHANGE BACK INTO MY SECRET IDENTITY ALTER EGO!

UH OH. SHE SAW THE LIGHT ON IN THIS ROOM. SHE'S COMING IN!
QUICK! GET IN THE COVERS! PRETEND WE'VE JUST BEEN READING IN BED!

BUT SHE KNOWS YOU ATTACKED HER AND RAN OUTSIDE HALF AN HOUR AGO!
THAT WAS **STUPENDOUS MAN**, NOT MILD-MANNERED CALVIN! *I'VE* BEEN IN BED WITH MY PJs ON SINCE 8:00.

YOU THINK SHE'S GOING TO BELIEVE *THAT*?
MY COVERS ARE HERE. MY PAJAMAS ARE **HERE**. IT'S AS PLAIN AS CAN BE!
WATERSON

ALL RIGHT! *I* FOUND YOU!
FOUND?? WHY, WHAT DO YOU MEAN? I'VE BEEN IN BED READING ALL EVENING WITH HOBBES.

DON'T GIVE ME THAT! YOU JUST NOW SNEAKED INSIDE, TOOK OFF YOUR SILLY COSTUME, AND JUMPED IN BED! I KNOW WHAT YOU DID! WELL YOU'RE GONNA GET IT ***NOW***, BUCKO!

OH YEAH? WHAT ARE YOU GOING TO DO TO ME, HUH? YOU CAN'T SEND ME TO BED WHEN I'M ALREADY ***IN*** BED! SORRY TO SPOIL YOUR FUN, YOU EEL!
WATERSON

OK, DOWNSTAIRS! ***MARCH!***
HEY, YOU CAN'T TAKE ME ***OUT*** OF BED! I NEED MY ***SLEEP!*** HEY! HEY!

WHILE YOUR DAD IS TAKING ROSALYN HOME, PERHAPS ***YOU'D*** LIKE TO EXPLAIN WHAT HAPPENED TONIGHT.

GOSH MOM, WHAT'S TO TELL? AT 8:00, I PUT ON MY PAJAMAS, BRUSHED MY TEETH AND WENT STRAIGHT TO BED. NOTHING HAPPENED.

AND THIS?
UH... ***LIES!*** ALL LIES! ROSALYN MADE ME DO THAT JUST SO I'D GET IN TROUBLE! SHE HATES KIDS! NONE OF THAT IS TRUE! I WENT STRAIGHT TO BED!

NICE TRY, PINOCCHIO.
WELL WHO WOUD'VE THOUGHT ROSALYN WOULD MAKE ME WRITE A FULL CONFESSION ?!
WATERSON

Calvin and HOBBES by WATTERSON

NO TV FOR A WEEK! WHAT INJUSTICE!

THEY THINK THEY'VE WON, BUT THEY HAVEN'T!
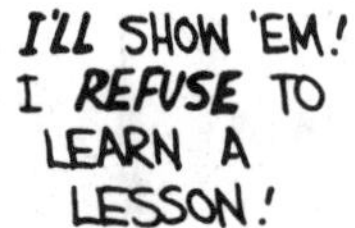
I'LL SHOW 'EM! I REFUSE TO LEARN A LESSON!
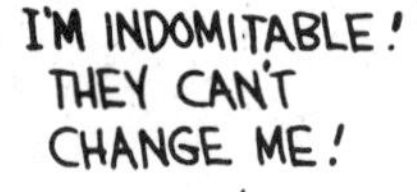
I'M INDOMITABLE! THEY CAN'T CHANGE ME!

I'LL SIT IN FRONT OF THE TV ALL WEEK EVEN IF I CAN'T TURN IT ON!

DAD, WILL YOU EXPLAIN THE THEORY OF RELATIVITY TO ME? I DON'T UNDERSTAND WHY TIME GOES SLOWER AT GREAT SPEED.

IT'S BECAUSE YOU KEEP CHANGING TIME ZONES. SEE, IF YOU FLY TO CALIFORNIA, YOU GAIN THREE HOURS ON A FIVE-HOUR FLIGHT, RIGHT?

SO IF YOU GO AT THE SPEED OF LIGHT, YOU GAIN MORE TIME, BECAUSE IT DOESN'T TAKE AS LONG TO GET THERE. OF COURSE, THE THEORY OF RELATIVITY ONLY WORKS IF YOU'RE GOING WEST.

GEE, THAT'S NOT WHAT MOM SAID AT ALL! SHE MUST BE TOTALLY OFF HER ROCKER.
WELL, WE MEN ARE BETTER AT ABSTRACT REASONING. GO TELL HER THAT.

MOM, CAN WE GO OUT TO THE HIGHWAY?
DO WHAT?

SEE, I'LL PUT ON MY ROLLER SKATES AND TIE A ROPE FROM THE CAR BUMPER TO MY WAIST. THEN WHEN I GIVE YOU THE HIGH FIVE, YOU PATCH OUT WHILE I RIDE BEHIND AT 55 MPH!

WHAT DO YOU SAY? CAN WE GO?

I SURE WISH YOU COULD DRIVE.

Calvin and HOBBES by WATTERSON
ACE PILOT SPACEMAN SPIFF CRUISES LOW OVER THE PLANET AT HIGH SPEED!

I WONDER WHAT THIS "E" ON THE FUEL GAUGE MEANS.

THE INTREPID SPACEMAN SPIFF LANDS ON PLANET GORZARG-5!

OUR HERO SETS OFF ACROSS THE DESOLATE TERRAIN IN SEARCH OF HELP! IN THE DISTANCE, METHANE CLOUDS RAIN SODIUM HYDROXIDE, A CAUSTIC ALKALI!

OH NO! THE DOWNPOUR WAS TOO HEAVY FOR THE GROUND TO ABSORB! A STEAMING RIVER OF CORROSIVE LIQUID RUSHES TOWARD OUR HERO!

THE BRAVE SPACEMAN SPIFF SCRAMBLES TO HIGHER GROUND, BUT THE FLOOD CONTINUES TO RISE!

OUR HERO IS TRAPPED! IT'S ONLY A MATTER OF TIME UNTIL THE FOAMING, NOXIOUS WASH CLEANS THE MEAT FROM SPIFF'S BONES! HOW COULD THINGS EVER GET WORSE?!
WATTERSON

AUGHH! AN ALIEN COMES TO PUSH HIM IN!
FOR HEAVEN'S SAKE, CALVIN! JUST GET IN!

WOW! NOBODY IS ON THE SWINGS! I CAN'T BELIEVE IT!

HA HA! I ALMOST *NEVER* GET A SWING AT RECESS!
THIS IS GREAT!
NO ONE IS TELLING ME TO HURRY UP!
HIGHER! HIGHER!
WHEE!

..EITHER THIS IS MY LUCKY DAY, OR I MISSED THE END-OF-RECESS BELL AGAIN.

HEY CALVIN, DIDN'T YOU SIGN UP TO PLAY BASEBALL AT RECESS?
NO, WHY?

YOU MUST BE THE ONLY BOY WHO DIDN'T. ALL THE OTHERS ARE PLAYING IN THE BACK FIELDS.
YOU MEAN I'M THE ONLY BOY ON A PLAYGROUND FULL OF *GIRLS*?!

IT SURE LOOKS LIKE IT. WANT TO RIDE ON THE TEETER-TOTTER WITH ME?
OH NO! I'M IN *COOTIE CENTRAL*! I HAVEN'T HAD MY SHOTS!

RELAX. STUPIDITY PRODUCES ANTIBODIES.
AIR FILTER! AIR FILTER!

WHY DIDN'T YOU SIGN UP TO PLAY BASEBALL LIKE THE REST OF THE BOYS? DON'T YOU LIKE SPORTS?
I DUNNO. I'D JUST RATHER RUN AROUND.

I HATE ALL THE RULES AND ORGANIZATION AND TEAMS AND RANKS IN SPORTS.

SOMEBODY'S ALWAYS YELLING AT YOU, TELLING YOU WHERE TO BE, WHAT TO DO, AND WHEN TO DO IT.

I FIGURE WHEN I WANT *THAT*, I'LL JOIN THE ARMY AND AT LEAST GET PAID.

Hey, lookit the sissy who didn't sign up for recess baseball!
I'M NOT A SISSY!

Oh yeah? You'd rather play dolls on the playground with girls.
I WASN'T PLAYING WITH DOLLS!

Sure you weren't! Let me see your Barbie doll, you sissy wimp!
I'M NOT A WIMP! IN FACT, I WAS GOING TO THE OFFICE TO SIGN UP FOR BASEBALL RIGHT NOW!

THEN AGAIN, IF I'M NOT A WIMP, WHY AM I TAKING THE PATH OF LEAST RESISTANCE?
OFFICE

I SIGNED UP TO PLAY BASEBALL EVERY RECESS, AND I DON'T EVEN LIKE BASEBALL THAT MUCH.

I MEAN, IT'S FUN PLAYING BASEBALL WITH JUST YOU, BECAUSE WE BOTH GET TO PITCH, BAT, RUN AND CATCH ALL AT ONCE. WE GET TO DO EVERYTHING.

MOSTLY WE JUST ARGUE OVER THE RULES WE MAKE UP! THAT'S THE PART I LIKE!
BUT THIS WILL BE WITH TEAMS AND ASSIGNED POSITIONS AND AN UMPIRE! IT'S BORING PLAYING IT THE REAL WAY!

DO YOU EVEN KNOW HOW TO PLAY THE REAL WAY?
SEE, THAT'S ANOTHER PROBLEM! SUPPOSE THEY MAKE ME A HALFBACK. CAN I TACKLE THE SHORTSTOP OR NOT?

I HEAR YOU SIGNED UP TO PLAY SOFTBALL AT RECESS.
YEAH, BUT I DIDN'T EVEN WANT TO. I JUST DID IT TO STOP GETTING TEASED.

WELL, SPORTS ARE GOOD FOR YOU. THEY TEACH TEAMWORK AND COOPERATION. YOU LEARN HOW TO WIN GRACIOUSLY AND ACCEPT DEFEAT. IT BUILDS CHARACTER.

EVERY TIME I'VE BUILT CHARACTER, I'VE REGRETTED IT! I DON'T WANT TO LEARN TEAMWORK! I DON'T WANT TO LEARN ABOUT WINNING AND LOSING! HECK, I DON'T EVEN WANT TO COMPETE! WHAT'S WRONG WITH JUST HAVING FUN BY YOURSELF, HUH?!

WHEN YOU GROW UP, IT'S NOT ALLOWED.
ALL THE MORE REASON I SHOULD DO IT NOW!

C'MON, LET'S GO OUTSIDE AND TRY SOME CATCHES BEFORE DINNER, OK? A LITTLE PRACTICE WILL MAKE YOU MORE CONFIDENT TOMORROW AT RECESS.
I HATE THESE FATHER-SON THINGS.

GO OUT A LITTLE BIT, AND I'LL HIT YOU A GROUNDER.
WHY DID I SIGN UP FOR THIS? I SHOULD JUST MOVE.

READY? NOW, BE SURE TO RUN UP TO THE BALL. DON'T JUST LET IT ROLL TO YOU.

ARE YOU OK? SOMETIMES THE BALL BOUNCES UP LIKE THAT, AND YOU'VE GOT TO BE READY.
THAGS FOR THE TIB, DAD. FIDE MY NODE AND PUD ID IN ICE SO THEY CAN SEW ID BAG OD!
WATTERSON

GOODNESS, WHAT HAPPENED?! YOU WERE ONLY OUT THERE A MINUTE!
A GROUNDER BOUNCED UP AND HIT CALVIN IN THE NOSE.

I'B BLEEDIG! BY ODE DAD ID TRYIG TO GILL ME!
HOLD YOUR HEAD BACK, HONEY. HERE'S SOME MORE TISSUES.

I'B NOD PLAYIG BADEBALL EDDY MORE! NEBBER AGAIN! I HADE IT!
SIT STILL SO THE BLEEDING CAN STOP, OK?
WATTERSON

I GUESS WE CAN FORGET HAVING A MILLIONAIRE BASEBALL PLAYER SUPPORT US IN OUR OLD AGE.
DEAR!
ALL BY CHARAGDER ID DRIPPIG OUT BY NODE!

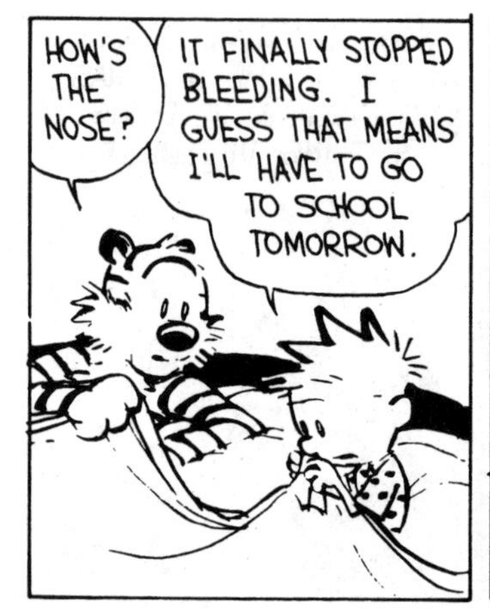
HOW'S THE NOSE?
IT FINALLY STOPPED BLEEDING. I GUESS THAT MEANS I'LL HAVE TO GO TO SCHOOL TOMORROW.

MY WHOLE LIFE IS A DISASTER. I GET INJURED JUST TRYING TO LEARN THE SKILLS IT TAKES TO PLAY A GAME I DON'T EVEN WANT TO PLAY!

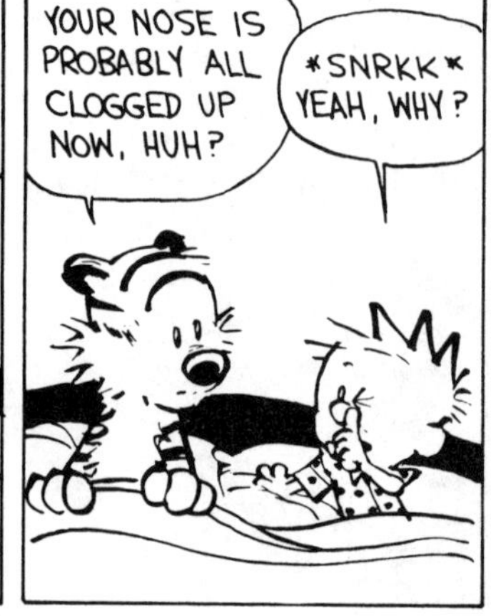
YOUR NOSE IS PROBABLY ALL CLOGGED UP NOW, HUH?
SNRKK YEAH, WHY?

IF YOU SNORE, I'M TILTING THE BED SO YOU ROLL OUT THE WINDOW.
IT'S ALWAYS NICE TO HAVE A SYMPATHETIC FRIEND TO TALK TO.
WATTERSON

I SEE YOU'RE BRINGING A GLOVE TODAY. DID YOU SIGN UP FOR RECESS BASEBALL?
YEAH, DON'T REMIND ME.

YOU'RE LUCKY THAT GIRLS DON'T HAVE TO PUT UP WITH THIS NONSENSE. IF A GIRL DOESN'T WANT TO PLAY SPORTS, THAT'S FINE!

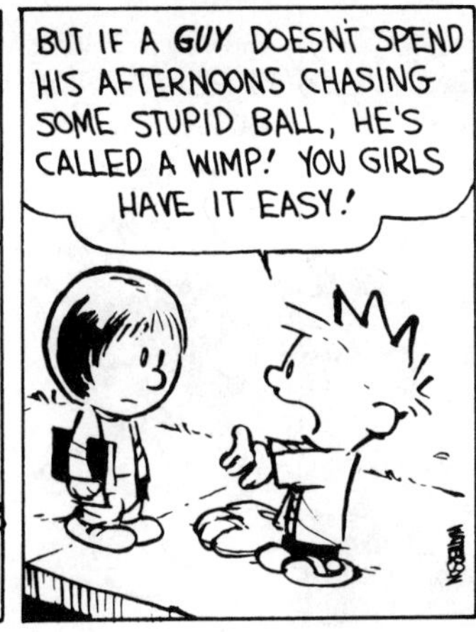
BUT IF A GUY DOESN'T SPEND HIS AFTERNOONS CHASING SOME STUPID BALL, HE'S CALLED A WIMP! YOU GIRLS HAVE IT EASY!

ON THE OTHER HAND, BOYS AREN'T EXPECTED TO SPEND THEIR LIVES 20 POUNDS UNDERWEIGHT.
AND IF YOU DON'T PLAY SPORTS, YOU DON'T GET TO MAKE BEER COMMERCIALS!

MR. LOCKJAW? I'M CALVIN. I'M SUPPOSED TO BE ON TEAM FIVE NOW.
OH YES, YOU'RE THE ONE WHO SIGNED UP LATE. HMM... OK, YOU GO PLAY LEFT FIELD.

LEFT FIELD. OK, I KNOW THAT. LET'S SEE, IF I'M HERE, THEN LEFT FIELD WOULD BE...
THAT WAY. PLAY DEEP LEFT FIELD.

I GUESS THIS IS PRETTY DEEP.

I THINK BASEBALL IS THE MOST BORING GAME IN THE WORLD. I'VE BEEN STANDING OUT HERE IN DEEP LEFT FIELD ALL THIS TIME, AND NOT A SINGLE BALL HAS COME OUT HERE!

ACTUALLY, I SUPPOSE THAT'S JUST AS WELL. I DON'T KNOW WHAT BASE TO THROW TO ANYWAY. IN FACT, I'M NOT EVEN SURE I CAN THROW THAT FAR.

HEY, WHAT'S EVERYONE DOING? ARE PEOPLE SWITCHING TEAMS, OR WHAT? THE GUYS AT BAT ARE NOW OUT HERE!

WELL, I'M SURE SOMEONE WOULD TELL ME IF I WAS SUPPOSED TO BE DOING ANYTHING DIFFERENT.

OUR HERO, THE FEARLESS SPACEMAN SPIFF, IS MAROONED ON THE MOST DISTANT PLANET IN THE GALAXY!

THERE'S NO HOPE OF RESCUE FROM THIS BLEAK AND ISOLATED WORLD!

OH, WHAT A DESOLATE PLACE TO BE TRAPPED! SPIFF TRIES DESPERATELY TO REPAIR HIS DISABLED SPACECRAFT!

CRACK
HIGH FLY TO LEFT FIELD! WHO'S OUT THERE?!
OUR HERO PAUSES. THERE'S SOME COMMOTION ON THE HORIZON. ALIENS! SPIFF GRABS HIS BLASTER!

WHERE'S THE LEFT FIELDER?!
SOMEBODY CATCH IT!
LEFT FIELD?! HEY, THAT'S ME!

WOW! A HIGH FLY RIGHT TO ME! I GOT IT! I GOT IT!

I CAUGHT IT!!
HE CAUGHT IT! IT'S AN OUT!
WAP!

I'M JUST A NATURAL ATHLETE, I GUESS.
HEY, WHO'S HE?
ISN'T HE ON THE OTHER TEAM?

HEY, LOOK WHO MADE THE OUT!
IT'S CALVIN!

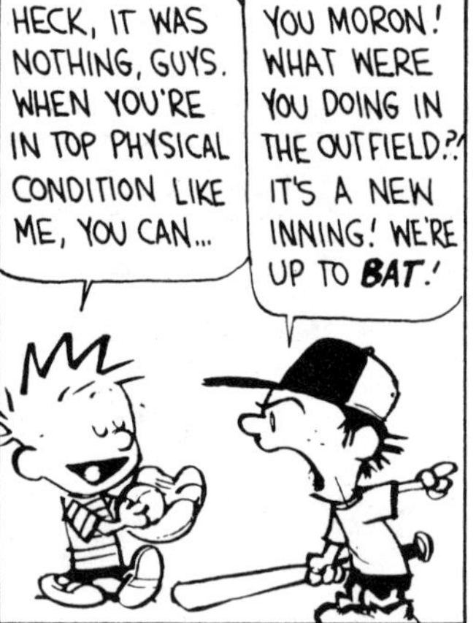
HECK, IT WAS NOTHING, GUYS. WHEN YOU'RE IN TOP PHYSICAL CONDITION LIKE ME, YOU CAN...
YOU MORON! WHAT WERE YOU DOING IN THE OUTFIELD?! IT'S A NEW INNING! WE'RE UP TO BAT!

HUH?
YOU CAUGHT THE BALL FOR THE WRONG TEAM! YOU GOT OUR OWN GUY OUT! WHAT A DWEEB! WHAT A JERK! WHAT AN IDIOT!

OOPS, I DROPPED THE CATCH. IT DOESN'T COUNT NOW, RIGHT?
GET HIM OFF OUR TEAM, MR. LOCKJAW!
CAN I HIT HIM WITH THE BAT? PLEASE? PLEASE??

HEY STUPID, IF YOU'RE GOING TO GET **OUR** GUYS OUT, WHY DON'T YOU JOIN THE OTHER TEAM?!
WHAT WERE YOU DOING IN THE OUTFIELD? DON'T YOU EVEN KNOW HOW TO PLAY?!

C'MON GUYS, IT'S JUST A **GAME**! THIS IS SUPPOSED TO BE FUN!
GAMES ARE ONLY FUN WHEN YOU **WIN**, BONE-HEAD! YOU'RE GONNA MAKE US **LOSE**!

IF YOU SCREW UP AGAIN, YOU'RE DEAD MEAT, CALVIN!
WHO TAUGHT YOU HOW TO PLAY ANYWAY? YOUR GRAND-MOTHER?
WAIT TILL I TELL THE OTHER TEAMS ABOUT **THIS**!

MR. LOCKJAW, I DON'T WANT TO PLAY ANY MORE. THERE'S TOO MUCH TEAM SPIRIT.
OK, QUITTER! GOODBYE.

I DON'T UNDERSTAND IT, HOBBES.

THE KIDS TEASED ME WHEN I **DIDN'T** PLAY BASEBALL. THEN THEY YELLED AT ME WHEN I **DID** PLAY. THEN THE TEACHER CALLED ME A "QUITTER" WHEN I **STOPPED** PLAYING.

UNLESS YOU'RE A STAR, YOU CAN'T PLEASE **ANY**ONE.

IN THAT CASE, WHY NOT JUST PLEASE YOUR-SELF?
BECAUSE MOM WON'T LET ME MOVE TO MADAGASCAR.

IT'S SATURDAY! WHAT DO YOU WANT TO DO?
ANYTHING BUT PLAY AN ORGANIZED SPORT.

WANT TO PLAY CALVINBALL?
YEAH!

NO SPORT IS LESS ORGANIZED THAN CALVINBALL!
NEW RULE! NEW RULE! IF YOU DON'T TOUCH THE 30-YARD BASE WICKET WITH THE FLAG, YOU HAVE TO HOP ON ONE FOOT!
12
4

Calvin and Hobbes
by WATTERSON
FASTER! FASTER!

THE TURBO IS POOPED.
THAT'S OK. GRAVITY JUST KICKED IN.

EVER NOTICE HOW DECISIONS MAKE CHAIN REACTIONS?
HOW SO?

WELL, EACH DECISION WE MAKE DETERMINES THE RANGE OF CHOICES WE'LL FACE NEXT.

TAKE THIS FORK IN THE ROAD FOR INSTANCE. WHICH WAY SHOULD WE GO? ARBITRARILY, I CHOOSE LEFT.

NOW, AS A DIRECT RESULT OF THAT DECISION, WE'RE FACED WITH ANOTHER CHOICE: SHOULD WE JUMP THIS LEDGE OR RIDE ALONG THE SIDE OF IT?

IF WE HADN'T TURNED LEFT AT THE FORK, THIS NEW CHOICE WOULD NEVER HAVE COME UP.
WATTERSON

I NOTE, WITH SOME DISMAY, YOU'VE CHOSEN TO JUMP THE LEDGE.
RIGHT. AND THAT DECISION WILL GIVE US NEW CHOICES.
LIKE, SHOULD WE BAIL OUT OR DIE IN THE LANDING?
EXACTLY. OUR FIRST DECISION CREATED A CHAIN REACTION OF DECISIONS. LET'S JUMP.

SEE? IF YOU DON'T MAKE EACH DECISION CAREFULLY, YOU NEVER KNOW WHERE YOU'LL END UP. THAT'S AN IMPORTANT LESSON WE SHOULD LEARN SOMETIME.
I WISH WE COULD TALK ABOUT THESE THINGS WITHOUT THE VISUAL AIDS.

TODAY FOR "SHOW AND TELL," I HAVE A SOUVENIR FROM THE AFTERLIFE! YES, YOU HEARD RIGHT! EQUALLY AMAZING IS MY OWN STORY OF YESTERDAY AFTERNOON, WHEN I ACTUALLY DIED OF BOREDOM!

I WAS DOING MY HOMEWORK, WHEN SUDDENLY I COLLAPSED! I FELT MYSELF RISING, AND I COULD SEE MY CRUMPLED BODY ON THE FLOOR. I DRIFTED UP IN A SHAFT OF LIGHT AND I ENTERED THE NEXT WORLD!

EVENTUALLY, MY HEART STARTED AGAIN AND I CAME BACK TO LIFE ... BUT NOT BEFORE BRINGING THIS BACK!
A YO-YO?

IT WAS PRETTY BORING THERE, TOO.
LET'S HAVE A LOOK AT THAT HOMEWORK.

AND SO, HAVING EATEN HER FILL, THE MOTHER BIRD RETURNS TO HER NEST...

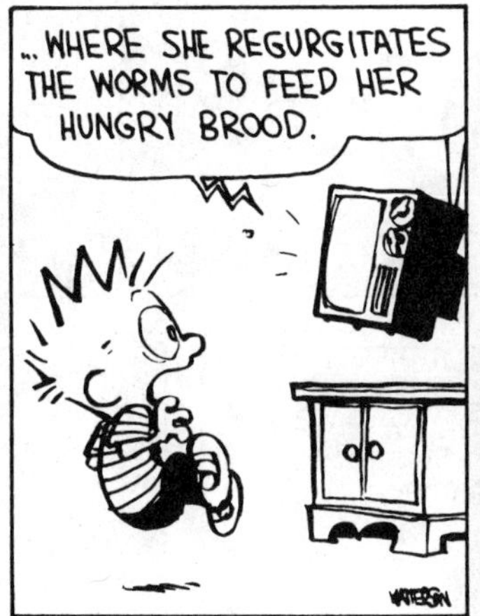
...WHERE SHE REGURGITATES THE WORMS TO FEED HER HUNGRY BROOD.

...SIGHHHHHH...

CALVIN, PAY ATTENTION!
AUGH

THERE'S NO HEAD REST ON THIS CHAIR! I SHOULD SUE FOR WHIPLASH!

Calvin and HOBBES
by WATTERSON
ARE YOU GOING TO READ CALVIN A STORY?
ONLY IF IT'S NOT THAT AWFUL "HAMSTER HUEY AND THE GOOEY KABLOOIE".

OH, BUT YOU LOOK SO **CUTE** DOING THE "HAPPY HAMSTER HOP"!
I DON'T **WANT** TO LOOK CUTE!!

WHAT STORY WOULD YOU LIKE TONIGHT, CALVIN?
I WANT A STORY ABOUT HOBBES AND ME.

OK... HMM.. LET'S SEE... ONCE THERE WAS A BOY NAMED CALVIN WHO LIVED WITH A TIGER NAMED HOBBES.
THIS IS GREAT!

TODAY THEY GOT UP AT THE CRACK OF DAWN AND MADE A HUGE RUCKUS RUNNING **UP** THE STAIRS, GALUMP, GALUMP, GALUMP, AND SLIDING **DOWN** AGAIN, BUMP, BUMP BUMP, BUMP!
YEAH, THEN THE **BIG BAD DAD** YELLED THAT IF WE DIDN'T KNOCK IT OFF, HE'D MAIL US TO **PLUTO** THIRD CLASS!

WHO'S TELLING THIS STORY, YOU OR ME?
YOU **DID** SAY THAT! DON'T TRY TO DENY IT!

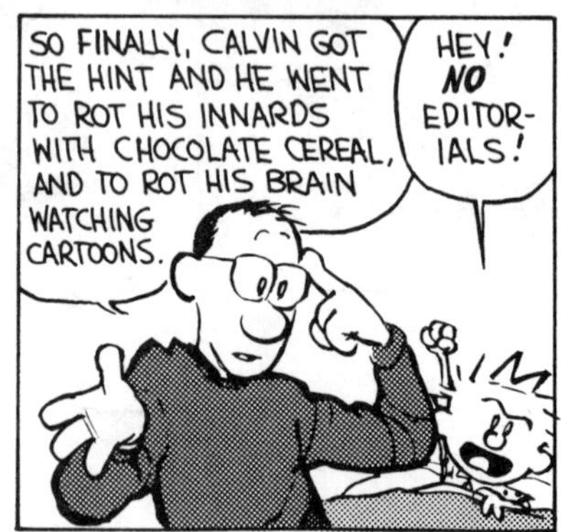
SO FINALLY, CALVIN GOT THE HINT AND HE WENT TO ROT HIS INNARDS WITH CHOCOLATE CEREAL, AND TO ROT HIS BRAIN WATCHING CARTOONS.
HEY! **NO** EDITORIALS!

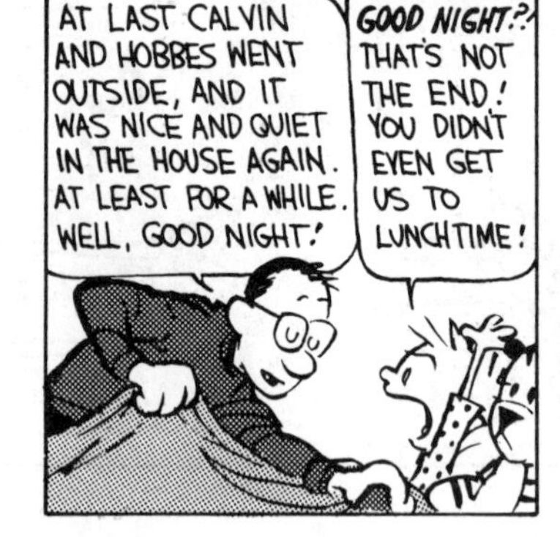
AT LAST CALVIN AND HOBBES WENT OUTSIDE, AND IT WAS NICE AND QUIET IN THE HOUSE AGAIN. AT LEAST FOR A WHILE. WELL, GOOD NIGHT!
GOOD NIGHT?! THAT'S NOT THE END! YOU DIDN'T EVEN GET US TO LUNCHTIME!

THAT'S RIGHT... IT'S NOT THE END OF THE STORY. THIS STORY DOESN'T **HAVE** AN END. YOU AND HOBBES WILL WRITE MORE OF IT TOMORROW AND EVERY DAY AFTER. BUT NOW IT'S TIME TO SLEEP, SO GOOD NIGHT.
OH! OK. GOOD NIGHT.

THIS **IS** A GOOD STORY ABOUT US IF IT DOESN'T END! THAT'S THE KIND OF STORY I LIKE BEST! GOOD NIGHT, OL' BUDDY!
ME TOO! SEE YOU TOMORROW!

HEY MOM, DID YOU FEEL ANYTHING FUNNY WHEN YOU GOT DRESSED TODAY?

FUNNY? WHAT DO YOU MEAN?
WELL, TICKLY MAYBE... OR SCRATCHY? ANYTHING LIKE A BITE OR A STING?

WHY? AND WHAT HAVE YOU GOT BEHIND YOUR BACK?!
UM... HERE, YOU MAY WANT THESE. WELL, HEH HEH, GOTTA RUN!

WOMEN! ALWAYS CHANGING THEIR CLOTHES!
AFTER I GET THAT KID, YOU'RE NEXT.

THIS TIME I'M REALLY GOING TO LEARN HOW TO RIDE THAT BICYCLE!

BALANCING ON TWO WHEELS IS JUST AS EASY AS BALANCING ON TWO FEE...
WHOA
OOMF!
BONK
ACKK
OW
I'D SAY THAT CROSSED THE LINE FROM IRONIC COINCIDENCE TO EVIL OMEN.

I DON'T WANT TO DO MY HOMEWORK. I WANT TO HAVE FUN.

TOO MUCH STRESS IS UNHEALTHY, YOU KNOW!
I DON'T SEE WHY I HAD TO COME IN.

Calvin and HOBBES by WATTERSON

I'M FREEEEEEEEEEEEEEEEEE

HO HO! THEY TRIED TO MAKE ME LEARN, BUT I WAS TOO TOUGH FOR 'EM!

I'M HOME!

WHY HELLO, CALVIN! DO COME IN, WON'T YOU?

CLICK.
HEY! HEY!

MAY I READ ALL YOUR COMIC BOOKS? I MAY? THANK YOU, CALVIN!

MAY I DRAW MUSTACHES ON ALL THE SUPERHEROES? I MAY? OH JOY!
I'LL GET HIM FOR THIS IF IT TAKES MY WHOLE LIFE.

I'VE COME UP WITH A NEW SYSTEM FOR DOING HOME-WORK. I CALL IT "EFFECTIVE TIME MANAGEMENT," OR "ETM" FOR SHORT.

I'VE DRAWN UP A SCHEDULE FOR EACH SCHOOL SUBJECT, AND I USE THIS KITCHEN TIMER TO MONITOR MY PACE.

THANKS TO ETM, I'M MUCH MORE EFFICIENT, AND MY WORK GOES FASTER!
RINGG

THERE! MY MATH MINUTE IS UP! SET THE CLOCK FOR MY SPELLING ASSIGNMENT, OK?
UM, YOUR SCHEDULE CALLS FOR SMALLER TIME INCREMENTS THAN THIS CLOCK CAN MEASURE.

NO I WON'T TAKE A PICTURE OF YOU.

KA

ZAM!

WHAT?

Calvin and HobbEs

by WATTERSON

TOAD STROGANOFF!

..EWWWW..
POKE POKE

AUGH!

CLINK
CLINK
CLINK

HA!

SPLORPP!

SPLAT!

DON'T BLAME **ME**. I'M THE ONE WHO SAID WE SHOULD CALL FOR A PIZZA.
WATTERSON

EWW! WHAT IS THIS?! IT LOOKS LIKE COMPOST!

MOM DOESN'T APPRECIATE ME.

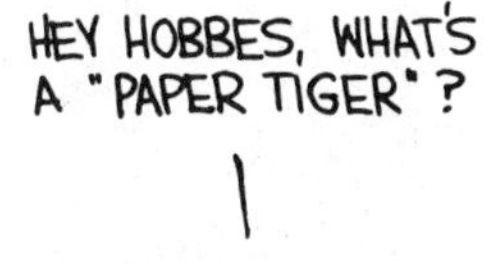
HEY HOBBES, WHAT'S A "PAPER TIGER"?

IT'S LIKE A PAPER BOY. YOU KNOW, A TIGER WITH A NEWSPAPER ROUTE.
OH.

THIS BOOK MAKES NO SENSE AT ALL.

HEY DAD, WOULD YOU PAY ME A DOLLAR TO EAT A BUG?

NO, YOU'D HAVE TO EAT A BUCKET OF BUGS BEFORE I'D PAY YOU A DOLLAR.

A WHOLE BUCKET?
OR I'D PAY YOU A DOLLAR TO PICK UP STICKS IN THE BACK YARD.

ALL MY REAL SKILLS ARE UNDERVALUED.

Calvin and HOBBES
by WATTERSON

WAK WAK
WAK
WAK WAK
WAK

F

GOOD DAY?
GETTING BETTER.
WATTERSON

ON DISTANT PLANET ZARK, WE FIND THE EMPTY RED SPACECRAFT OF OUR HERO, THE BOLD SPACEMAN SPIFF!

UH OH! UP AHEAD, THE ROCKS ARE CHARRED WITH DEATH RAY BLASTS! A VIOLENT STRUGGLE TOOK PLACE HERE!

AND ONLY THE TRACKS OF A LARGE, SINISTER ALIEN LEAVE THE SCENE! WHAT HAS HAPPENED TO THE EARTHLING EXPLORER?

CALVIN, THIS IS HUMILIATING!!
I DON'T WANT TO GO! PUT ME DOWN!

SPACEMAN SPIFF IS BEING HELD PRISONER BY HIDEOUS ALIENS! WHAT DO THEY WANT WITH HIM?

SPIFF IS SOON TO FIND OUT! OUR HERO IS CALLED BEFORE THE ALIEN POTENTATE!

..WHERE IT BECOMES CLEAR THAT SPIFF IS ABOUT TO BE SACRIFICED...

..TO APPEASE THE EVIL GOD THEY CALL "NOLLIJ"!
UP TO THE BLACKBOARD. HURRY UP.

STARING DEATH IN THE FACE, OUR HERO THINKS FAST.
11-4=

INCHING CLOSER TO THE SACRIFICIAL PIT, SPIFF SLOWLY AND SMOOTHLY REACHES FOR THE TINY ATOM BLASTER CONCEALED IN HIS BELT!

YAA! ALL RIGHT, YOU BLOODSUCKING, MUTANT CHROMOSOMAL DISASTERS! NOBODY MOVE! I'M OUTTA HERE!

CALVIN, GIVE ME THAT RUBBER BAND RIGHT THIS MINUTE!
I SAID NOBODY MOVE!

SPIFF ESCAPES! THE DANK AND SMELLY CORRIDORS OF THE ALIEN FORTRESS ARE DESERTED! ALL THE ALIENS HAD GATHERED FOR THE SPECTACLE OF OUR HERO'S DEMISE!

THE FEARLESS SPACE EXPLORER MAKES IT TO THE PLANET SURFACE, BUT THE ALIEN QUEEN IS IN PURSUIT!
CALVIN, GET BACK HERE!

SPIFF JUMPS INTO THE COCKPIT, PRESSURIZES THE LAUNCH THRUSTERS, AND...

BLASTS OFF! OUR HERO IS SAFE!
Tomorrow: OR IS HE ??

CALVIN! WHAT ARE YOU DOING HOME?! IT'S NOT EVEN NOON!

UH, THEY LET US OUT EARLY TODAY. THERE WAS, UM, A GAS LEAK.
WHAT?! DOES ANYONE KNOW YOU LEFT?! I'M CALLING THE SCHOOL.

DON'T WASTE YOUR TIME! EVERYONE WAS EVACUATED! THERE'S NOBODY THERE!
HELLO? ELEMENTARY SCHOOL OFFICE, PLEASE.

OUR HERO HADN'T COUNTED ON RUNNING INTO A ZARK ENFORCER SHIP! SPIFF'S EVASIVE MANEUVERS COME TO NAUGHT! THIS COULD BE THE END!

BOY, I SURE GOT IN BIG TROUBLE TODAY! MOM HIT THE ROOF WHEN SHE FOUND OUT I JUST LEFT SCHOOL.

WHAT HAPPENED?

SHE DROVE ME BACK AND WE HAD TO TALK TO MY TEACHER AND THE PRINCIPAL! THEY TALKED ABOUT MY STUDY HABITS, AND NOW I'VE GOT EXTRA HOMEWORK!

OOH.
AND DAD IS GOING TO CHECK IT EVERY NIGHT TO MAKE SURE IT'S DONE RIGHT! CAN YOU BELIEVE IT?!

SO TRY TO DO AN EXTRA GOOD JOB NOW, OK?
YOU'RE LUCKY TIGERS ARE SO SMART.

Calvin and Hobbes

by WATTERSON

OLLY-WOLLY POLLIWOGGY UMP-BUMP FIZZ!
HEY!

HA HA! I STOLE YOUR FLAG!
BUT I HIT YOU WITH THE CALVIN BALL! YOU HAVE TO PUT THE FLAG BACK AND SING THE "I'M VERY SORRY" SONG!

I DON'T HAVE TO SING THE SONG! I WAS IN THE "NO SONG" ZONE!
NO YOU WEREN'T. I TOUCHED THE "OPPOSITE POLE", SO THE "NO SONG ZONE" IS NOW A "SONG ZONE"!

I DIDN'T SEE YOU TOUCH THE OPPOSITE POLE! YOU HAVE TO DECLARE IT!
I DECLARED IT OPPOSITELY BY NOT DECLARING IT. START SINGING.

"HERE'S THE 'VERY SORRY SONGG.' WON'T YOU HELP AND SING ALONGG?"
BUM BUM BUM

I BLEW IT! I KNEW IT! I'M VERY VERY SORRY THAT I TOOK YOUR PRECIOUS FLAAGGG!
..... HE'S SORRY! ..... SO SORRY! JUST DON'T DO IT ANY MORE, YOU SCURVY SCALAWAAGGG!

I'M FREE! I GET FREE PASSAGE TO WICKET FIVE!
NO, THAT'S WHAT WE DID LAST TIME, REMEMBER?

OH YEAH. HMM.

OK, THE NEW RULE IS WE HAVE TO JUMP EVERYWHERE UNTIL SOMEONE FINDS THE BONUS BOX!
THAT'S GOOD!

THE ONLY PERMANENT RULE IN CALVINBALL IS THAT YOU CAN'T PLAY IT THE SAME WAY TWICE!
THE SCORE IS STILL Q TO 12!
WATTERSON

Calvin and Hobbes by WATTERSON

ANOTHER PLANET, ANOTHER SWEEPING PANORAMA OF INDESCRIBABLE GRANDEUR!

THE INCREDIBLE SPACEMAN SPIFF ZOOMS TO THE SURFACE OF AHNOOIE-4!

TOUCHING DOWN, OUR HERO SETS OFF TO SEARCH FOR SENTIENT LIFE!

ALAS, SPACEMAN SPIFF ONLY DISCOVERS A HIDEOUS BLOB SO MONUMENTALLY STUPID THAT IT JUST STARES STRAIGHT AHEAD, COMPLETELY UNAWARE OF ANYTHING AROUND IT!

COMPASSIONATELY, OUR HERO DECIDES TO PUT THE BLOB OUT OF ITS MISERY. SPIFF SETS HIS BLASTER ON "LIQUEFY."

EWW! MISS WORMWOOD! CALVIN'S SHOOTING SPIT BALLS!

PERPLEXED BY THE BLOB'S RESILIENCE, SPIFF ADDS MORE JUICE AND PREPARES TO FIRE AGAIN!
WATTERSON

UFOs! ARE THEY REAL?? HAVE THEY LANDED IN OUR TOWNS AND NEIGHBORHOODS?

DO THE CHILLING PHOTOGRAPHS BY AN AMATEUR PHOTOGRAPHER REALLY SHOW A SINISTER ALIEN SPACESHIP AND THE GRIM RESULTS OF A CLOSE ENCOUNTER, OR ARE THE PICTURES AN ELABORATE HOAX?

LISTEN TO AN EXPERT ON SPACE ALIENS SPECULATE ON THEIR HIDEOUS BIOLOGY AND THEIR HORRIFYING WEAPONRY! ALL THIS AND MORE...

...ON CALVIN'S SHOW AND TELL ... NEXT!
CALVIN, WILL YOU COME HERE PLEASE?

TWITCHING TUFTED TAIL, A TOASTY, TAWNY TUMMY: A TIRED TIGER.

...AN ALLITERATIVE HAIKU BY CALVIN. THANK YOU, THANK YOU.

SHEESH.

YOU KNOW HOW PEOPLE LOOK AT MODERN ART AND ALWAYS SAY, "MY 6-YEAR-OLD KID COULD DO THAT!"?

WELL, THAT GAVE ME THIS GREAT IDEA! I'VE DECIDED TO BECOME A FORGER AND GET RICH PASSING OFF FAKE PAINTINGS TO MUSEUMS!
A LOT OF PAINTINGS SELL FOR TENS OF MILLIONS OF DOLLARS NOW, SO I MAKE A PRETTY GOOD HOURLY RATE.

YOU SHOULD PROBABLY SCRATCH OUT THE COPYRIGHT DATE ON THE CARTOON STATIONERY.
OOH YEAH, GLAD YOU CAUGHT THAT!

Calvin and Hobbes

by WATTERSON

HISTORICAL MARKER
"CALVIN'S HOUSE"
IN JANUARY, SOME 40 SNOWMEN MET A GRUESOME FATE ON THIS SPOT.

EVERY DAY I LOOK FOR A MOVING VAN HERE.

KNOCK KNOCK

GREAT MOONS OF NEPTUNE! A FOOL MORTAL FEMALE!
CALVIN?

I'M NOT CALVIN! I'M STUPENDOUS MAN! FRIEND OF FREEDOM! OPPONENT OF OPPRESSION!
UH HUH. WHAT ARE YOU DOING?

I WAS JUST ABOUT TO USE MY STUPENDOUS POWERS TO LIBERATE SOME COOKIES BEING HELD HOSTAGE ON THE TOP SHELF OF THE PANTRY! NOW IF YOU'LL EXCUSE ME, DUTY CALLS!

SLAM!

A BOLT OF CRIMSON STREAKS ACROSS THE SKY! THE MAN OF MEGA-MIGHT IS OFF TO SAVE THE DAY!

DID THEY HAVE AN EGG YOU COULD BORROW?
NO ONE WAS HOME, MOM.

"ONCE UPON A TIME THERE WAS..."
HOLD IT. THIS STORY DOESN'T HAVE ANY SHOOT-UPS IN IT, DOES IT?

YOU MEAN GUNS? NO.
ANY VIOLENCE AT ALL?

UM... NOT REALLY.
ANY REFERENCES TO SATANISM? ANY PROFANITY? ANY CAR CHASES? ANY LEWD PARTS?

OF COURSE NOT!
WHAT MAKES YOU THINK I'LL LIKE THIS?

HEY MOM, WANT TO SEE SOMETHING GREAT?

WITH ONE SIP FROM THIS ORDINARY CAN OF SODA, I CAN BURP FOR ALMOST TEN SECONDS STRAIGHT!

CALVIN, I DON'T...
BUT THAT'S NOT ALL! AT THE SAME TIME, I'LL ALSO RECITE A GROSS LIMERICK I LEARNED AT SCHOOL! ...READY?

MAYBE IF YOU RECITED THE GETTYSBURG ADDRESS...
FORGET IT. MY TALENTS ARE WASTED ON HER KIND.

WELL, LOOK WHO'S UP! GOOD MORNING SLEEPYHEAD!

YOU'VE MISSED THE BEST PART OF THE DAY! I'VE BEEN UP SINCE 6:30 GETTING MANY THINGS ACCOMPLISHED!

AT LEAST WHEN I HAVE A DAY OFF, I CAN TELL THE DIFFERENCE.

I JUST KNOW SOME NURSE SWITCHED THE BASSINETS.

Calvin and HOBBES
by WATTERSON
MY LIFE COULD BE A LOT BETTER THAN IT IS.

I'M HAPPY, BUT IT'S NOT LIKE I'M **ECSTATIC**.

LIFE IS LIKE TOPOGRAPHY, HOBBES. THERE ARE SUMMITS OF HAPPINESS AND SUCCESS...

...FLAT STRETCHES OF BORING ROUTINE...

...AND VALLEYS OF FRUSTRATION AND FAILURE.

BUT *I'M* DEDICATING MYSELF TO EXPERIENCING ONLY **PEAKS**! I WANT MY LIFE TO BE ONE NEVER ENDING ASCENSION!

EACH MINUTE OF EVERY DAY SHOULD BRING ME GREATER JOY THAN THE PREVIOUS MINUTE!

I SHOULD ALWAYS BE SAYING, "MY LIFE IS BETTER THAN I EVER IMAGINED IT WOULD BE, AND IT'S ONLY GOING TO IMPROVE."

I'M JUST GOING TO JUMP FROM PEAK TO PEAK! I'M... WHOOPS.

AT LEAST WITH FLAT PLACES, YOU DON'T HAVE SO FAR TO GO DOWN.
ONLY **LOSERS** GO DOWN! FOR ME IT'S ONLY GOING TO BE **UP** AND **UP**!

CLICK.

PANDER TO ME!

PLAYING A RECORD? I'LL SHOW YOU SOMETHING INTERESTING.

COMPARE A POINT ON THE LABEL WITH A POINT ON THE RECORD'S OUTER EDGE. THEY BOTH MAKE A COMPLETE CIRCLE IN THE SAME AMOUNT OF TIME, RIGHT?
YEAH...

BUT THE POINT ON THE RECORD'S EDGE HAS TO MAKE A BIGGER CIRCLE IN THE SAME TIME, SO IT GOES FASTER. SEE, TWO POINTS ON ONE DISK MOVE AT TWO SPEEDS, EVEN THOUGH THEY BOTH MAKE THE SAME REVOLUTIONS PER MINUTE!

ON YOUR MARK.. GET SET... GO!

I'M GOING SO SLOW, I'M MOVING BACKWARD! I'M WINNING!
THAT'S CHEATING!

Calvin and Hobbes

by WATTERSON

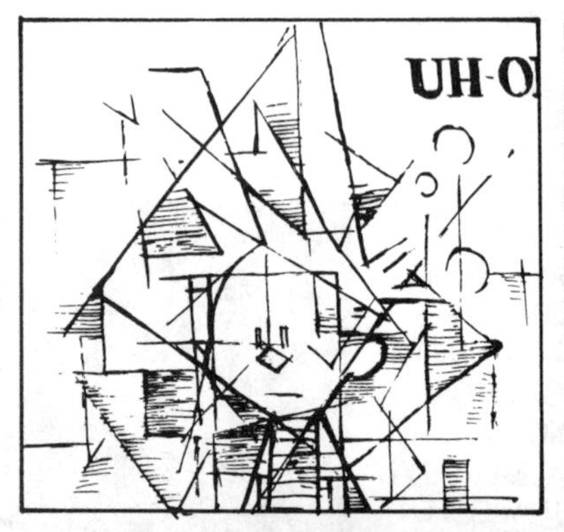
UH-O

OH NO! EVERYTHING HAS SUDDENLY TURNED NEO-CUBIST!
COMICS

IT ALL STARTED WHEN CALVIN ENGAGED HIS DAD IN A MINOR DEBATE! SOON CALVIN COULD SEE BOTH SIDES OF THE ISSUE! THEN POOR CALVIN BEGAN TO SEE BOTH SIDES OF EVERYTHING!

THE TRADITIONAL SINGLE VIEWPOINT HAS BEEN ABANDONED! PERSPECTIVE HAS BEEN FRACTURED!

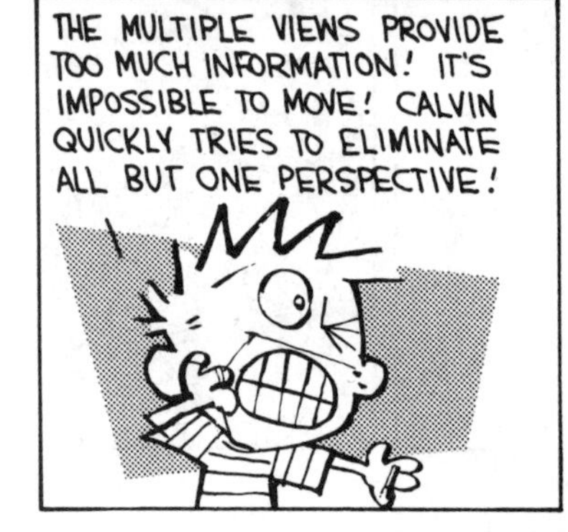
THE MULTIPLE VIEWS PROVIDE TOO MUCH INFORMATION! IT'S IMPOSSIBLE TO MOVE! CALVIN QUICKLY TRIES TO ELIMINATE ALL BUT ONE PERSPECTIVE!

IT WORKS! THE WORLD FALLS INTO A RECOGNIZABLE ORDER!

YOU'RE STILL WRONG, DAD.

HELLO?
HI DAD!

CALVIN, IS THIS IMPORTANT?
OOPS. WAIT. FORGET I CALLED YOU "DAD," OK? THIS ISN'T CALVIN.

CALVIN, I'VE GOT WORK TO DO. I'LL SEE YOU WHEN I GET HOME, OK? GOODBYE.
WAIT! DO YOU HAVE ANY CRIMES TO REPORT?

PHOOEY. THIS SECRET IDENTITY STUFF IS HARD TO GET USED TO.

WANT TO SEE SOMETHING COOL? I'VE GOT A BABY TOOTH THAT'S JUST HANGING BY A THREAD...

...AND I CAN TURN IT ALL THE WAY AROUND WITH MY TONGUE...

...OR MAKE IT SWING FROM SIDE TO SIDE! SEE? SEE?

THEY'RE ALL JUST JEALOUS.

LOOK!

I DON'T SEE ANYTHING.
YOU MISSED IT. WELL, I'M DONE.

WHAT DID HE SEE?
AN OPPORTUNITY.

Calvin and HOBBES
by WATTERSON

OH CALVIN, WOULD YOU PLEASE EMPTY THIS IN THE GARAGE TRASH CAN?

BOY, SOME VACATION **THIS** SUMMER IS!

HOP IN, HOBBES! WE'RE GOING TO GET RICH!

OH NO, I'M NOT GETTING IN THAT BOX. I DON'T WANT TO BE TRANSMOGRIFIED OR DUPLICATED OR WHATEVER.

WHAT? WHEN THE **TOP** IS OPEN, IT'S A TIME MACHINE, REMEMBER?
EVEN WORSE.

OH, DON'T BE SUCH A BABY. THE WAY YOU ACT, YOU'D THINK THE DINOSAUR ACTUALLY **GOT** US LAST TIME. WHY, IT WASN'T EVEN A CARNIVORE.
I DON'T CARE. YOU AND THAT BOX ARE PLAIN BAD NEWS.

TOO BAD YOU'RE NOT GOING BACK TO THE JURASSIC WITH ME. AN OPPORTUNITY LIKE THIS DOESN'T COME ALONG EVERY DAY, YOU KNOW.

THE LESS OFTEN, THE BETTER, IS WHAT **I** SAY.
WE'RE JUST GOING ON A PHOTO SAFARI! WHEN WE COME BACK WITH **REAL** DINOSAUR PHOTOS, WE'LL GET RICH!

YOU CAN DROP THE "WE" STUFF. I'M NOT GOING.
OK, WELL, I GUESS I'LL HAVE TO EAT ALL THESE GREAT SNACKS MYSELF THEN.

SNACKS? WHAT **KIND** OF SNACKS? ARE THEY **GOOD** SNACKS? HOW MANY SNACKS DID YOU BRING??
NEVER MIND! YOU SAID YOU'RE NOT GOING.

I GUESS IF WE GET TO HAVE SNACKS, IT WOULD BE OK TO TIME TRAVEL. IF THEY'RE **GOOD** SNACKS, I MEAN.
GREAT! PUT ON YOUR VORTEX GOGGLES.

THE DIAL IS SET FOR 140 MILLION YEARS AGO, SO
OFF WE GO-O-O!

I HAVE A QUESTION. WHY DON'T WE GET YOUNGER AS WE GO BACK IN TIME, AND DISAPPEAR AS WE PASS THE DAY WE WERE BORN?

I'D EXPLAIN IT, BUT THERE'S A LOT OF MATH.
I THOUGHT YOU GOT A "D" IN MATH.

SEE, THESE PHOTOS WILL ANSWER HUNDREDS OF QUESTIONS ABOUT DINOSAUR ANATOMY AND BEHAVIOR! PALEONTOLOGISTS WILL PAY THROUGH THE NOSE TO SEE THESE!

WHAT'S **THIS** UGLY BRUTE CALLED?
AN ALLO-SAUR!

I'M RIGHT HERE. YOU DON'T NEED TO SHOUT.
RUN!

WHEN WE GET TO THE TIME MACHINE, THROW HIM THE SNACKS WE PACKED! MAYBE THAT WILL DIVERT HIM WHILE WE TAKE OFF!

YOU CAN THROW **YOUR** SNACKS. I MIGHT STILL WANT MINE.
YOU'RE GOING TO BE A SNACK YOURSELF! GET IN! GET IN!

QUICK! THROW HIM THE FOOD!
MY SANDWICH HAD MUSTARD. IS THIS ONE YOURS?

PUT ON YOUR VORTEX GOGGLES! WE'RE TAKING OFF!
EWW, THIS BANANA IS MUSHY. HE CAN HAVE **THIS**.

WE DID IT! WE'RE OFF!
HERE.

BOY, THAT WAS A CLOSE CALL, BUT IT WILL BE WORTH IT WHEN WE GET THESE PICTURES DEVELOPED.
SINCE I RESCUED YOUR SANDWICH, CAN I EAT IT?

HEY MOM, GUESS WHERE HOBBES AND I HAVE BEEN!

I **SAW** WHERE YOU WERE. YOU WERE PLAYING IN A CARDBOARD BOX OUT BACK.
NOPE! THAT'S JUST WHAT IT **LOOKED** LIKE.

WE TIME-TRAVELED TO THE JURASSIC, BUT WE RETURNED AT THE SPLIT SECOND WE LEFT! THAT'S WHY IT DIDN'T LOOK LIKE WE WERE GONE! WE SAW LOTS OF DINOSAURS!

WELL, YOU'VE HAD A PRODUCTIVE MORNING THEN.
YEAH. WILL YOU TAKE THIS FILM TO BE DEVELOPED? I'LL PAY YOU BACK WHEN TIME MAGAZINE COUGHS UP FOR MY STORY.

HOBBES, LOOK! WE GOT OUR PICTURES BACK FROM OUR JURASSIC TRIP!
OH BOY! LET'S SEE!

WOW, THESE CAME OUT GOOD! LOOK AT THAT APATOSAUR!
THERE'S ME! THERE'S ME!

YES! YES! WE'RE **RICH**! HA HA! NOW WE CAN GET OUR OWN APARTMENT!
THIS DINOSAUR BLINKED.

I'LL BUY A CAR TOO, BUT SINCE I CAN'T DRIVE FOR ANOTHER DECADE, WE'LL HAVE TO GET A CHAUFFEUR.
IF WE PAY HIM, HE HAS TO LET US SIT UP FRONT AND BEEP THE HORN, RIGHT?

WELL DAD, IT'S TOO BAD YOU WEREN'T ANY NICER TO ME ALL THESE YEARS.

BEG PARDON?
YEP, I CAN'T SAY I'M PARTICULARLY INCLINED TO SHARE MY FUTURE MILLIONS WITH YOU. HERE, LOOK.

DINOSAURS?
HOBBES AND I WENT TO THE JURASSIC TODAY AND CAME BACK WITH THESE DRAMATIC PHOTOGRAPHS! WE'RE GOING TO BE RICH!

I DIDN'T REALIZE DINOSAURS LOOKED SO SMALL AND PLASTIC.
HEY, WHAT ARE YOU INSIN-UATING?!

DAD DOESN'T BELIEVE WE WENT TO THE JURASSIC AND TOOK PHOTOGRAPHS OF REAL DINOSAURS.

HE SAYS IT LOOKS LIKE WE JUST PUT MY TOY MODELS IN THE YARD AND TOOK PICTURES OF **THEM**! HE SAYS OUR GET-RICH-QUICK SCHEME WON'T WORK.

HUH!
HE SAID IF WE **REALLY** WANTED TO GET SOME MONEY, HE'D PAY US A DOLLAR TO PULL WEEDS OUT OF THE FRONT WALK.

JUST A DOLLAR?
OF COURSE I TOLD HIM WE DIDN'T WANT THE MONEY **THAT** BAD.

Calvin and HOBBES
by WATTERSON

ANOTHER ONE OF THESE DAYS.

UH OH! IN ANOTHER OF LIFE'S MYSTERIOUS QUIRKS, CALVIN FINDS HIMSELF AN INCH TALL ON THE WRITING DESK!

HIS ONLY HOPE IS TO TEAR OFF A SHEET FROM A NEARBY PAD OF PAPER!

AT HIS TINY SIZE, FOLDING THE SHEET IS DIFFICULT, BUT SOON CALVIN'S PATIENCE IS REWARDED!

HE PUSHES OFF AND CATCHES A SMALL THERMAL RISING UP THE FRONT OF THE DESK!

A GUST FROM AN OPEN WINDOW SENDS CALVIN SOARING ACROSS THE HOUSE!

THERE'S DAD! LEAN! LEAN!

YES! CALVIN IS ABLE TO STEER! THIS SHOULD GET DAD'S ATTENTION!

I DON'T NEED PARENTS. ALL I NEED IS A RECORDING THAT SAYS, "GO PLAY OUTSIDE!"
WATTERSON

The End